Macmillan McGraw-Hill

California Mathematics 4

Homework Practice and Problem-Solving Practice Workbook

Macmillan/McGraw-Hill

TO THE TEACHER These worksheets are the same ones found in the Chapter Resource Masters for *California Mathematics, Grade 4*. The answers to these worksheets are available at the end of each Chapter Resource Masters booklet.

 **Macmillan McGraw-Hill**

Send all inquiries to:
Macmillan/McGraw-Hill
8787 Orion Place
Columbus, OH 43240

ISBN: 978-0-02-111968-4
MHID: 0-02-111968-6

Homework Practice/Problem Solving Practice Workbook, Grade 4

Printed in the United States of America.

15 16 17 18 19 PRS 19 18 17 16 15 14

Table of Contents

Name _____ Date _____

Homework Practice

Place Value Through Hundred Thousands

Write each number in *standard form*.

1. three hundred twenty-six thousand, four hundred fifty-one.

_____

2. one hundred forty-five thousand, two hundred thirty-seven.

_____

Write each number in *word form* and *expanded form*.

3. 87,192

_____

_____

4. 413,750

_____

_____

Complete the *expanded* form.

5. 91,765 = 90,000 + _____ + 700 + _____ + 5

6. 798,054 = 700,000 = _____ + 8,000 + _____ + 4

Write the value of each underlined digit.

7. 645,<u>8</u>02 _____

8. 27<u>1</u>,385 _____

Spiral Review   Divide. (Previous Grade)

9. $10 ÷ 2 _____

10. 16 ÷ 4 _____

11. 9 ÷ 3 _____

12. 25 ÷ 5 _____

13. 8 ÷ 1 _____

14. 36 ÷ 6 _____

15. 7)‾42‾ _____

16. 5)‾40‾ _____

17. 3)‾21‾ _____

18. 9)‾81‾ _____

19. 7)‾35‾ _____

20. 8)‾32‾ _____

Name _____ Date _____

Problem-Solving Practice

4NS1.1

Place Value Through Hundred Thousands

Solve.

1. Michael says he has used 42,567 pencils since he started school. Maria wants to be sure she heard the number correctly. Write 42,567 in word form and in expanded form for Maria.

   _____

   _____

2. Emily and Inez found a treasure map that shows the location of gold coins. They want to show their friends how much gold they can find. Write the number in standard form. 200,000 + 70,000 + 4,000 + 600 + 90 + 3 _____

3. Javier and Nick want to start a dog-walking business after school. They made 1,236 flyers to hand out around their neighborhood. Write the number in word form and in expanded form.

   _____

   _____

4. Union Township has a population of 1<u>7</u>2,650. What is the value of the underlined digit? _____

5. Jan's grandfather was a pilot. He estimates that he has flown 460,500 miles in his life. When Jan told her mother about this, Jan said 406,500 miles. Jan's mother said she should get her numbers right. What mistake did Jan make? How can Jan fix it?

   _____

   _____

   _____

Name _____ Date _____

Homework Practice

Place Value Through Millions

Write each number in *standard form*.

1. four hundred thirty-two million, five hundred eighty-six thousand, six hundred twelve. _____

2. nine hundred fifty-seven million, two hundred four thousand, three hundred eighty-one. _____

Write each number in *word form* and *expanded form*.

3. 103,721,495

_____

_____

_____

4. 682,364,518

_____

_____

_____

_____

Write the value of each underlined digit.

5. 5<u>6</u>1,754,908 _____   6. 49<u>8</u>,749,013 _____

7. <u>7</u>,020,154 _____   8. <u>3</u>98,216,045 _____

Spiral Review

Write the number in *standard form*. (Lesson 1-1)

9. two hundred forty-three thousand, seven hundred eighteen

_____

10. six hundred ninety-five thousand, eighty-seven _____

Complete the *expanded form*.

11. 198,045 = 100,000 + 90,000 + _____ + 40 + _____

12. 982,105 = 900,000 + _____ + 2,000 + _____ + 5

Name _____ Date _____

Problem-Solving Practice

Place Value Through Millions

Solve.

1. Hannah read that 11,765,825 people saw the L.A. Lakers play last season. Chris wants to be sure he heard the number correctly. Write 11,765,825 in word form and in expanded form for Chris.

   _____

   _____

   _____

2. There are approximately 200,000,000 + 90,000,000 + 8,000,000 + 800,000 + 60,000 + 9,000 + 500 + 2 people living in the United States. Write the number in standard form. _____

3. Approximately 37,124,871 people live in California. Write the number in word form and in expanded form.

   _____

   _____

   _____

   _____

4. The pirate movie made 1\underline{3}$5,634,554 in one weekend. What is the value of the underlined digit? _____

5. American car makers produce 5,650,000 cars each year. In a report, Ben wrote that Americans made 6,550,000 cars. What mistake did Ben make? How can he fix it?

   _____

   _____

   _____

Name _____ Date _____

Homework Practice

Problem-Solving Strategy

Solve. Use the *four-step plan*.

1. Luis can ride his bike to school three different ways. When he goes with Christina, it takes 22 minutes. When he goes with Devin, it takes 17 minutes. When he goes by himself, it takes 12 minutes. How much faster can Luis get to school when he rides by himself than with Christina?

   _____

2. Marissa wants to buy her brother a present. The store has a $10 soccer ball, a $9 baseball bat, an $18 baseball glove, a $13 tennis racket, and a $21 helmet. If Marissa has $15, which presents could she buy?

   _____

3. Inez can carry 2 bags of groceries into her home with each trip from the car. Her brother can carry the same amount. How many trips will it take them to carry 28 bags of groceries?

   _____

4. Carlos wants to go to Happy Land Park with 4 friends at the end of summer. Tickets are $18 for children. How much will it cost for Carlos and his friends to go to Happy Land Park?

   _____

Spiral Review

Write each number in *standard form*. (Lesson 1-2)

5. five hundred eighty-seven million, one hundred forty-two thousand, eight hundred sixty-six

   _____

6. one hundred twenty million, five hundred seventy-four thousand, two hundred seventy-five

   _____

Write the value of each underlined digit.

7. 3<u>1</u>6,113,276 _____ 8. 67,<u>5</u>12,327 _____

Name _____ Date _____

Homework Practice

Compare Whole Numbers

Compare. Use >, <, or =.

1. 1,347 ◯ 1,317

8. 234,582 ◯ 23,458

2. 5,781 ◯ 5,872

9. 366,438 ◯ 366,843

3. 8,091 ◯ 8,901

10. 672,809 ◯ 672,809

4. 11,654 ◯ 1,654

11. 702,593 ◯ 702,359

5. 77,215 ◯ 77,215

12. 894,710 ◯ 89,470

6. 97,604 ◯ 96,407

13. 1,436,721 ◯ 1,346,721

7. 111,280 ◯ 112,800

14. 23,086,543 ◯ 23,806,543

15. 527,308,516 ◯ 523,708,500

16. fifty-two thousand, four hundred sixty-seven ◯ 502,467

17. 800,000 + 60,000 + 400 + 60 + 2 ◯ 97,642

18. four million, two hundred twelve thousand, thirty-two ◯
4,000,000 + 9,000 + 50 + 9

19. 6,821,054 ◯ sixteen million, five hundred twelve thousand,
eight hundred fourteen

Spiral Review

Solve. (Lesson 1-3)

20. Jake delivers 234 newspapers a week. Miranda delivers
477 newspapers a week. How many more newspapers does
Miranda deliver than Jake?

Name _____ Date _____

Problem-Solving Practice

Compare Whole Numbers

Solve.

1. Charles is moving from Springfield, which has 482,653 people, to Greenville, which has 362,987. Is he moving to a larger or smaller city? Explain.

   _____

   _____

2. The Denver Mint made 2,638,800 pennies. The Philadelphia Mint made 2,806,000 pennies. Which mint made more pennies?

   _____

3. About 450,000 people lived in Maryville in 2000. In 2005, about 467,000 people lived in Maryville. Did the number of people living in Maryville get larger or smaller?

   _____

4. In 1950, bike stores sold about 205,850 bikes. In 2000, bike stores sold about 185,000 bikes. Is the number of bikes being sold getting larger or smaller?

   _____

5. In 2000, about 290,000,000 cans of soda were sold each day. In 1970, about 65,000,000 cans were sold each day. Were more cans of soda sold in 2000 or 1970? Explain.

   _____

   _____

6. Allison found out that the average American works about 2,100 hours a year. The average French worker works about 1,650 hours a year. Who works more hours?

   _____

Name _____ Date _____

Homework Practice

Order Whole Numbers

Order the numbers from *greatest* to *least*.

1. 5,827; 5,628; 5,835; 5,725

_____

2. 17,472; 18,451; 19,629; 17,784

_____

3. 34,893; 37,230; 29,167; 38,173

_____

4. 273,280; 267,902; 275,784; 270,562

_____

5. 478,024; 478,165; 475,907; 477,281

_____

Solve.

6. Christine is writing a report about the world's largest animals. Order these animals by weight from greatest to least to help her decide which animal to write about first.
   Blue whale: 418,878 lb   African elephant: 11,023 lb
   White rhinoceros: 4,850 lb   Indian elephant: 8,818 lb

_____

_____

7. Nicole wants to learn more about the islands of the world. Order these islands from greatest to least.
   Borneo 287,300 mi   Madagascar 227,000 mi
   New Guinea 309,000 mi   Greenland 839,999 mi

 **Spiral Review**

Compare. Use >, <, or =. (Lesson 1–4)

8. 907,654 987,421   9. 1,235,903  1,237,903

Name _____ Date _____

Problem-Solving Practice

Order Whole Numbers

Solve.

1. For the state high school basketball tournament, the teams are divided into groups based on the size of their high school. Order these high schools from most students to least. Then name the two teams that are from the largest high schools.

   Fremont: 2,759   Kingsville: 1,865
   Jefferson: 2,341   La Plata: 2,056

   _____

   _____

   _____

2. Madison wants to know which sports are most popular in California. She reads a list that shows how many kids play each sport. Order the sports from most players to least to help show Madison which sports are popular.

   Soccer: 3,875,026   Lacrosse: 900,765

   Surfing: 250,982   Basketball: 2,025,351

   _____

3. Tyler wondered how many people voted in the United States Presidential elections. He wants to know which year had the fewest voters in the last four elections. Order the election years from least to greatest number of voters.

   2004:   122,295,345   1996:   96,456,345
   2000:   105,586,274   1992:   104,405,155

   _____

4. Rosa's science teacher challenged the class to reduce the amount of electricity they used. First, students needed to find out how much they were using. Order the students from who used the most electricity to who used the least.

   Rosa: 3,056 kwh   Anna: 3,098 kwh
   Austin: 3,125 kwh   Robert: 3,105 kwh

   _____

Name _____ Date _____

Homework Practice

Round Whole Numbers

Round each number to the given place-value position.

1. 623; ten _____

2. 435; ten _____

3. 581; hundred _____

4. 870; hundred _____

5. 1,302; hundred _____

6. 1,447; hundred _____

7. 2,398; thousand _____

8. 4,628; thousand _____

9. 23,876; thousand _____

10. 31,098; thousand _____

11. 44,872; ten thousand _____

12. 65,281; ten thousand _____

13. 124,830; ten thousand _____

14. 237,524; hundred thousand _____

15. 497,320; hundred thousand _____

16. 1,567,438; hundred thousand _____

17. 2,802,746; hundred thousand _____

18. 3,458,321; thousand _____

19. 4,872,018; ten thousand _____

20. 6,873,652; thousand _____

Solve.

21. There are 572 beans in the jar. Carolina guesses there are 600 beans in the jar. Steven estimates there are 500 beans in the jar. Rounding to the hundred, who estimated correctly?

_____

Spiral Review

Order from *greatest* to *least*. (Lesson 1-5)

22. 564; 623; 276

_____

23. 3,560; 3,542; 3,498; 3,589

_____

24. 64,890; 65,032; 64,217; 64,578

_____

25. 213,093; 212,764; 213,570; 213,435

_____

Name _____ Date _____

Problem-Solving Practice

4NS1.3

Round Whole Numbers

Solve.

1. Taipei 101 in Taiwan is 1,673 feet tall. How tall is this building when rounded to the nearest hundred? the nearest thousand?

   _____

2. The Golden Gate Bridge spans about 4,224 feet. Brian says the bridge spans about 4,000 feet. Samantha says it spans about 4,200 feet. Their teacher says they are both correct. How is this possible? _____

   _____

3. The Lake Mead reservoir at the Hoover Dam covers 157,900 acres. How large is Lake Mead rounded to the nearest hundred thousand?

   _____

4. Ricardo estimates there are 10,000 balls in the ball pit at the park. His father helps him count the 12,345 balls. Is Ricardo's estimate good if he rounds to the nearest ten thousand? Is it good if he rounds to the nearest thousand? Explain. _____

   _____

   _____

5. Experts estimate that there are 500,000 leopards living in the wild. If we were able to count all the leopards and found 527,863 leopards, would the 500,000 estimate be a good estimate? Explain.

   _____

   _____

6. Gabriella has 15,467 coins she has collected from around the world. Her friends asked her about how many coins were in her collection. What would be a good answer for her to tell them? Explain.

   _____

   _____

Name _____ Date _____

Homework Practice

Problem-Solving Investigation

Use any strategy shown below to solve. Tell which one you used.

- Use the four-step plan
- Draw a picture
- Look for a pattern
- Make a table

1. Alexis and Tyler are getting a dog. They like labradors, golden retrievers, and dalmatians. Their mother said they can get the smallest dog. The average labrador is 70 pounds. The average golden retriever is 65 pounds. The average dalmatian is 55 pounds. Which dog will Alexis and Tyler get?

_____

2. Marisol sells candy bars to raise money for her softball team. Each day she sells more. The first day she sells 5. The second day she sells 6. The third day she sells 8. The fourth day she sells 11. The fifth day she sells 15. The sixth day she sells 20. How many will she sell on the tenth day? _____

3. Erica was searching for her sunglasses. She walked 2 blocks north, 3 blocks south, 4 blocks east, and 3 blocks west. How many blocks did she walk? How far is Erica from where she began her search?

_____

_____

4. Paige and her 3 friends want to go to the movies on Saturday. If tickets are $6 each, how much will it cost for all 4 friends to go to the movies? _____

Spiral Review

Round each number to the given place-value position. (Lesson 1-6)

5. 4,563; hundred _____

6. 7,412; hundred _____

7. 12,763; thousand _____

8. 67,924; ten thousand _____

9. 137,654; ten thousand _____

10. 472,917; hundred thousand _____

11. 2,348,915; thousand _____

12. 4,712,634; ten thousand _____

Name _____ Date _____

Homework Practice

Algebra: Addition Properties and Subtraction Rules

Complete each number sentence. Identify the property or rule used.

1. $15 + 0 =$ _____

_____

2. $6 + 13 = 13 +$ _____

_____

3. _____ $- 0 = 7$

_____

4. $(5 + 3) + 7 = 5 + ($ _____ $+ 7)$

_____

5. $7 + 9 + 3 = 9 + 3 +$ _____

_____

6. $12 -$ _____ $= 12$

_____

Spiral Review

Solve. (Lesson 1–7)

7. Alonso earns $6 each day walking his aunt's dog. He is saving to buy a mountain bike helmet for $24. How many days will Alonso need to work to buy his mountain bike helmet? _____

8. Every night Anna reads for 10 minutes before going to sleep. How many minutes does Anna read in 2 weeks? _____

9. Marta's sunflower is 12 inches taller than her sister Vanessa's plant. If Vanessa's plant is 4 inches tall, how tall is Marta's sunflower? _____

10. Sarah's basketball games are 4 quarters that are each 12 minutes long. Is it possible for Sarah to play 45 minutes in a game? How do you know?

_____

Name _____ Date _____

Problem-Solving Practice

Algebra: Addition Properties and Subtraction Rules

Solve.

1. While bird watching, Gabrielle saw 6 robins, 4 cardinals, and 3 blue jays. Chase saw 3 robins, 6 blue jays, and 4 cardinals. Who saw more birds? _____

_____

2. For homework, Brooke has 15 math problems, 5 social studies problems, and 9 science problems. Use mental math to determine how many problems she has for homework. Tell what property you used.

_____

_____

_____

_____

3. Jose needs to leave in 85 minutes to go to a movie. Before he leaves, he has to finish his homework, which takes 22 minutes; clean his room, which takes 18 minutes; walk the dog, which takes 35 minutes; and take out the trash, which takes 5 minutes. Does Jose have enough time to do all of these before he leaves? Find the sum mentally. Tell what property you used.

_____

_____

_____

_____

4. A soccer team scored 2 goals in the first half. If they won the game by a score of 2 to 1, how many goals did they score in the second half? Tell what property you used.

_____

_____

Name _____ Date _____

Homework Practice

Estimate Sums and Differences

Round to the indicated place value.

1. 4,854 + 8,138; hundreds

_____

2. 887 − 678; tens

_____

3. 8,752 + 3,269; thousands

_____

4. 7,799 − 3,431; thousands

_____

5. 436 − 218; tens

_____

6. 9,118 + 1,615; hundreds

_____

7. $163.18 + $387.69; tens

_____

8. $442.87 − $259.14; hundreds

_____

9. $6,841.18 + $2,152.69; thousands

_____

10. $9,326.54 + $6,971.48; thousands

_____

The table shows the driving distances between some major U.S. cities.

New York City, NY to Chicago, IL	800 miles
Chicago, IL to Los Angeles, CA	2,090 miles

11. Austin is planning a trip over summer vacation. About how many miles will his family drive if they go from New York City to Chicago and then to Los Angeles? Round your answer to the nearest hundred.

_____

 **Spiral Review**

Complete each number sentence. Identify the property or rule shown. (Lesson 2–1)

12. 25 − _____ = 0

_____

13. 54 + _____ = 54

_____

14. 9 + 3 + 7 = 7 + 9 + _____

_____

15. (12 + _____) + 11 = 12 + (7 + 11)

_____

Name _____ Date _____

Problem-Solving Practice

Estimate Sums and Differences

Solve.

1. The parking lot in front of the school has 53 parking spaces. The parking lot in the back of the school has 38 spaces. About how many parking spaces are there? Round your answer to the nearest ten.

_____

2. A total of 691 people attended the school play. 521 people attended the band concert. About how many more people attended the play than the concert? Round your answer to the nearest hundred.

_____

3. A sweater costs $18.95. A skirt costs $32.35. About how much does a sweater and a skirt cost? Round your answer to the nearest ten.

_____

4. On Wednesday, 37 students played kickball. On Thursday, 28 students played kickball. About how many students played kickball on Wednesday and Thursday? Round your answer to the nearest ten.

_____

5. The highest point in Texas, Guadalupe Peak, is 8,749 feet high. The highest Point in California, Mount Whitney, is 14,494 feet high. About how much higher is Mount Whitney then Guadalupe Peak? Round your answer to the nearest thousand.

_____

6. Christina spent $20.25 on 3 tickets to the fair. She also spent $15.78 on food and $33.25 for the rides. About how much did Christina spend at the fair? Round your answer to the nearest ten.

_____

Name _____ Date _____

Homework Practice

4MR2.5, 4NS3.0

Problem-Solving Skill

Tell whether an estimate or an exact answer is needed. Then solve.

1. Carlota is going to her friend's house after her soccer game. It takes her 18 minutes to shower and change clothes. Then it takes her 31 minutes to get to her friend's house. If her game is over at 2:00 p.m., about what time will she arrive at her friend's house?

_____

2. Monica and her family went to the movies on Saturday. Adult tickets cost $7.50 and children's tickets cost $4.25. How much did they spend if they bought two adult tickets and one children's ticket?

_____

3. A minor league baseball team wanted to determine if they set a new attendance record for a weekend. The first game had an attendance of 13,209 people. The second game had an attendance of 12,489 people. What was the combined attendance for both games?

_____

Spiral Review

Estimate. Round to the nearest hundred. (Lesson 2–2)

4. $886 - 174 =$ _____

5. $612 + 914 =$ _____

6. $826 - 590 =$ _____

Estimate. Round to the nearest thousand.

7. $7,378 - 5,903 =$ _____

8. $22,358 - 14,699 =$ _____

9. $8,723 - 4,235 =$ _____

10. $2,799 + 11,089 =$ _____

Name _____ Date _____

Homework Practice

Add Numbers

Find each sum.

1. 651
    + 274 _____

5. 5,239
    + 2,794 _____

2. $727.75
    + $657.35 _____

6. 169,748
    + 355,470 _____

3. 219
    + 566 _____

7. $41.89
    + $54.32 _____

4. 12,887
    + 8,364 _____

8. $2,991
    + $3,799 _____

Spiral Review

Tell whether an estimate or an exact answer is needed. Then solve. (Lesson 2–3)

9. John and his father are building a birdhouse. They need one 12-inch long piece of wood, one 17-inch long piece of wood, and one 9-inch long piece of wood. How many inches of wood do John and his father need to buy?

    _____

10. Mercedes and her mom spent $12.00 for tickets to a soccer game. They also spent $16.87 on food and $23.36 on souvenirs. About how much did they spend?

    _____

11. John wants to build a model car. The kit for the car costs $19.34, glue costs $10.30, and paint costs $11.25. About how much money does he need to build the car?

    _____

2-4

Problem-Solving Practice

4NS3.1

Add Numbers

Solve.

1. In 2003 the population of Cedar Park, Texas was 41,482 and the population of College Station, Texas was 73,536. What was the combined population of Cedar Park and College Station?

_____

2. A school fundraiser made $877.21 on pizza sales and $487.36 on wrapping paper sales. How much money did the fundraiser make?

_____

3. A zoo has two elephants, Sally and Joe. Sally weighs 7,645 pounds and Joe weighs 12,479 pounds. How much do Sally and Joe weigh in all?

_____

4. In December, New York City had 3 inches of snow. In January and February the city had 8 inches of snow each month. In March, the city has 2 inches of snow. How many inches of snow fell during December, January, February, and March?

_____

5. At a library 1,324 children's books, 1,510 fiction books, and 912 non-fiction books were checked out. How many books were checked out of the library?

_____

6. Colin spent 35 minutes mowing the lawn, 22 minutes trimming the bushes, and 12 minutes watering the flowers. How long did it take Colin to do the yard work?

_____

Name _____ Date _____

Homework Practice

Subtract Numbers

Chapter Resources

Subtract. Use addition to check.

1.   940
       − 271 _____

3. $821.13
       − $569.74 _____

5.   9,516
       − 7,228 _____

2. $61.48
       − $15.75 _____

4.   644
       − 361 _____

6.   33,539
       − 31,649 _____

7. $98.54 − $52.79 _____

8. 6,637 − 2,846 _____

Solve.

9. John Stennis was a senator from Mississippi. He was first elected to the U.S. Senate in 1947. He served in the Senate until 1989. How long was he a senator? _____

Spiral Review

Find each sum. (Lesson 2–4)

10.   651
       + 274 _____

13. $39.12
       + $21.99 _____

11.   9,446
       + 4,187 _____

14. $23.58
       + $9.65 _____

12.   366
       + 749 _____

15.   41,927
       + 53,157 _____

Name _____ Date _____

Problem-Solving Practice

Subtract Numbers

Solve.

1. There are 635 people in the stadium when the football game starts. Before the game is over, 213 people leave early. How many people remained to see the end of the game?

_____

2. Miranda buys lunch for herself and a friend for $13.57. If she hands the cashier $20.17, how much change will she get back?

_____

3. In 2006, it had been 230 years since the United States became a nation. In what year did the United States become a nation?

_____

4. Sierra took 83 free throws during the basketball season. If she missed 34 of them, how many free throws did she make?

_____

5. Alicia had $112.78 in her bank account. She bought a present for her sister for $22.54 and a present for her brother for $24.69. How much money does she have in her account now?

_____

6. As a promotion, a minor league baseball team is giving out 1,250 free hats. If 2,359 people attended the game, how many did not get a hat?

_____

Name _____ Date _____

Homework Practice

Problem-Solving Investigation

Tell whether an estimate or exact answer is needed. Then solve.

1. Thomas has 324 coins in his coin collection. Mia has 297 in her coin collection. About how many do they have together?

_____

2. Mrs. Ramirez bought sweaters for her children. She spent $23, $28, and $34 on the sweaters. About how much did she spend on sweaters?

_____

3. Maya had $45. She bought a skirt for $25 and a book for $14. How much money does she have left?

_____

4. Fernando's class has 25 students in it. Will's class has 5 more than Fernando's. How many students does Will's class have?

_____

5. Niko has bought 7 pairs of socks in the last year. If each pair of socks costs about $4, how much has he spent?

_____

Spiral Review

Find each difference. Use addition or estimation to check. (Lesson 2–5)

6. 780 − 456 _____

7. $45.90 − $33.99 _____

8. 459 − 83 _____

9. 1,405 − 222 _____

10. $598.33 − $330.54 _____

Name _____ Date _____

Homework Practice

Subtract Across Zeros

Subtract. Use addition to check.

1. 500
    − 360 _____

2. 800
    − 279 _____

3. $13.00
    − $6.37 _____

4. 1,100
    − 628 _____

5. 4,000
    − 1,731 _____

6. 3,300
    − 1,892 _____

7. 8,000
    − 6,313 _____

8. 3,000
    − 1,811 _____

9. $140.00
    − $108.92 _____

10. 9,000
     − 5,281 _____

Spiral Review

Tell whether an estimate or exact answer is needed. Then solve. (Lesson 2–6)

11. The flowers cost $9, the clay pot costs $29, and the bag of soil costs $7. About how much does it cost to plant the flowers in all?

_____

12. Jamal had 17 baseball cards. After he gave some of the cards to his brother, he had 9 cards left. How many baseball cards did Jamal give to his brother?

_____

Name _____ Date _____

Problem-Solving Practice

Subtract Across Zeros

Solve.

1. In a 90-minute soccer game Jorge played 72 minutes. How long was he on the sideline?

   _____

2. If 700 tickets were sold to a concert and only 587 people attended, how many people bought a ticket but did not go?

   _____

3. In a chess tournament, 400 players take part in the first round. During the second round, 274 players take part. How many players did not make the second round?

   _____

4. The Amazon River is 4,000 miles long. The Snake River is 1,038 miles long. How much longer is the Amazon River than the Snake River?

   _____

5. Logan has a gift card for $200. He spends $45.89 on Monday and $61.30 on Tuesday. How much money is left on his gift card?

   _____

6. Luisa takes $75 to the amusement park. She spends $29.95 on a ticket, $13.21 on food, and $22.78 on a T-shirt. How much money does she have left?

   _____

Name _____ Date _____

Homework Practice

Addition and Subtraction Expressions

Find the value of each expression if $y = 7$ and $b = 2$.

1. $y + 6$

4. $14 - b$

7. $(y - 1) + 3$

_____

2. $b + 8$

5. $y + 18$

8. $19 - (b + 3)$

_____

3. $y - 2$

6. $12 + b$

9. $y + (14 - 9)$

_____

Write an expression for each situation.

10. four more than j _____

11. v minus fifteen _____

12. the sum of k and twelve _____

13. twenty-three subtracted from x _____

Write an expression for each situation. Then find the value of the expression to answer the question.

14. John walks 5 minutes longer to school than Rosa. If Rosa walks 24 minutes to school, how long does John walk to school?

_____

15. Caroline is 7 inches shorter than Kevin. Kevin is 56 inches tall. How tall is Caroline?

_____

Spiral Review

Find each difference. (Lesson 2–7)

16. $200 - 106 =$ _____

19. $\$80.00 - \$23.21 =$ _____

17. $6,000 - 3,265 =$ _____

20. $7,000 - 5,936 =$ _____

18. $500 - 483 =$ _____

21. $300 - 129 =$ _____

Name _____ Date _____

Problem-Solving Practice

Addition and Subtraction Expressions

Solve.

1. Ming and Amy count the total number of beads they have. Ming has 21 beads. Write an expression to show the total number of beads that Ming and Amy have all together.

   _____

2. Julie has 16 paper clips. She gives away x number of paper clips. Write an expression for the number of paper clips she has left.

   _____

3. Each week, Hector sends 2 E-mails to his friend Chet. He also sends E-mails to other friends each week. Write an expression to show how many E-mails Hector sends each week.

   _____

4. George and his brother have a total of 8 CDs. If George has n CDs, write an expression to show how many CDs his brother has.

   _____

5. Delia saves $2 from her weekly allowance. She also saves the money she earns from delivering newspapers each week. Write an expression to show her total weekly savings. If she earns $5 delivering newspapers this week, how much money does she save in all this week?

   _____

Name _____ Date _____

Homework Practice

Solve Equations Mentally

Solve each equation mentally.

1. $3 + d = 11$ _____

2. $f + 4 = 10$ _____

3. $13 - h = 4$ _____

4. $j - 2 = 19$ _____

5. $6 + m = 17$ _____

6. $15 - r = 2$ _____

7. $20 = t + 7$ _____

8. $9 = w - 12$ _____

9. $12 = 3 + z$ _____

10. $17 - b = 4$ _____

Write and solve an equation for each situation.

11. A number plus 5 equals 13. What is the number?

_____

12. Twelve less than a number equals 25. What is the number?

_____

13. The sum of 4 and a number is 27. What is the number?

_____

14. Seven subtracted from a number is 15. What is the number?

_____

Spiral Review

Find the value of each expression if $x = 6$ and $c = 4$. (Lesson 3-1)

15. $x + 3$ _____

16. $c + 12$ _____

17. $x - 5$ _____

18. $10 + c$ _____

19. $(x - 2) + 7$ _____

20. $22 - (c + 3)$ _____

Write an expression for each situation.

21. seven more than d _____

22. w minus 12 _____

23. the sum of f and seventeen _____

24. twenty-one subtracted from p _____

Name _____ Date _____

Problem-Solving Practice

Solve Equations Mentally

Write and solve an equation for each situation.

1. Tad had $10. He spent some of his money on a model car. If Tad has $4 left, how much money did the model car cost?

_____

2. A large puzzle costs $12. A small puzzle and a large puzzle together cost $18. How much would you pay for 1 small puzzle?

_____

3. Nadine bought some new CDs. She has 15 other CDs. She now has 20 CDs. How many CDs did she buy?

_____

4. Emma collected 18 rocks. She gave some to her sister. Emma has 12 rocks left. How many rocks did she give her sister?

_____

5. Tony rented some movies. He watched 2 movies over the weekend. He has 6 movies left. How many movies did Tony rent?

_____

6. Kameko scored 12 points in the first half of a basketball game. At the end of the game, he had a total of 25 points. How many points did Kameko score in the second half of the game?

_____

7. Laura planted 20 flowers in her garden. A rabbit ate some of the flowers. Laura has 11 flowers left. How many flowers did the rabbit eat?

_____

Name _____ Date _____

Homework Practice

Problem-Solving Skill

Identify any missing or extra information. Then solve if possible.

1. At the kennel, the staff walks each dog 2 times per day. They walk 3 dogs at a time. How many dogs do they take for a walk each day?

_____

_____

2. Each week, Michelle will invite 1 girl from her class to come home with her. There are 17 boys in her class and 16 (including Michelle) girls. How many weeks will it take to invite every girl in her class?

_____

_____

3. Patrick loves vegetables. Every day for school he packs a small bag of carrots, a small bag of celery, and a small bag of broccoli. He also likes apple juice. How many small bags of vegetables does Patrick bring to school in a week?

_____

_____

4. Nicole wants to buy a turkey sandwich, chips, and a bottle of water for lunch. She has $5.00 with her. Does she have enough?

_____

_____

Spiral Review

Solve each equation mentally. (Lesson 3-2)

5. $5 + d = 9$ _____

6. $f + 7 = 20$ _____

7. $16 - h = 5$ _____

8. $j - 7 = 12$ _____

9. $5 + m = 14$ _____

10. $22 - r = 7$ _____

11. $24 = t + 6$ _____

12. $12 = w - 11$ _____

13. $9 = 4 + z$ _____

14. $18 = 11 + t$ _____

Name _____ Date _____

Homework Practice

Algebra: Find a Rule

Complete the input/output table for each equation.

1.

Rule: $e + 7 = f$	
Input (e)	Output (f)

2.

Rule: $g - 4 = h$	
Input (g)	Output (h)

Input (s)	Output (f)
2	$27
4	$29
6	
8	
10	

3. A dance studio offers lessons to students. It costs $25 to rent the studio plus $1 per student. Use the table to write an equation for this situation. _____

4. Find how much it will cost if 6, 8, and 10 students take lessons.

_____

Spiral Review   Identify any missing or extra information. Then solve if possible. (Lesson 3-3)

5. Every day Pedro wears a different baseball cap to school. He has red hats, black hats, and blue hats. How many weeks will it take for him to wear all of his hats?

_____

Name _____ Date _____

Problem-Solving Practice

Algebra: Find a Rule

The table shows how many people will be going on a field trip.

Input (s)	Output (p)
25	29
27	31
29	33
31	
33	

1. Jessica's class is going on a field trip. The school will bring all the students who are there that day plus 4 chaperones. Use the table to write an equation for this situation. _____

2. Find how many people will go if there are 31 and 33 students going. _____

3. Write a new equation if the school will bring the students and 6 chaperones. _____

4. Create a table for the new equation. How many people will go if 35 students go on the trip?

Input (s)	Output (p)

_____

Name _____ Date _____

Homework Practice

4MR2.3, 4NS3.0

Problem-Solving Investigation

Use any strategy shown below to solve. Tell which strategy you used.
- Draw a picture
- Make a table
- Look for a pattern

1. Allison can read 4 pages of her book in 8 minutes. How many minutes will it take her to read 16 pages of her book?

   _____

   Strategy: _____

2. Richard can clean his room in 22 minutes. Corey can clean his room in 25 minutes, and Brooke can clean her room in 21 minutes. If they have to clean their rooms twice a week, how many minutes do all three spend cleaning their rooms each week?

   _____

   Strategy: _____

3. Complete the number pattern.

   45, 43, 42, 40, 39, ____, ____, ____, ____

   Strategy: _____

Create an input/output table for each equation. (Lesson 3-4)

4. $e + 5 = f$ 5. $g - 8 = h$

Rule: $e + 5 = f$	
Input (e)	Output (f)

Rule: $g - 8 = h$	
Input (g)	Output (h)

3–6

Homework Practice

Balanced Equations

4AF2.1

Find the missing number in each equation.

1. 7 + 5 = 7 + _____

2. 12 + 9 = 12 + _____

3. 15 + 6 = 4 + 11 + _____

4. 20 + 8 = 13 + 7 + _____

5. 36 + 3 = 20 + 16 + _____

6. 27 + 6 = 15 + 12 + _____

7. 48 + 4 = 22 + 26 + _____

8. 16 + 9 = 8 + _____ + 9

9. Tyrone spins a spinner numbered 0 through 5. He spins a 3 and a 5 for a total of 8 points. Gloria spins a 5 on her first try. What number does Gloria need to spin to get a total equal to Tyrone? _____

10. Bonnie earned $14 and $18 dollars the last two times she babysat. Kara earned $10 and $4 the last two times she babysat. How much more money does Kara need to earn to equal the total amount Bonnie earned? _____

Spiral Review

Use any strategy shown below to solve. Tell which strategy you used. (Lesson 3-5)

- Draw a picture
- Look for a pattern
- Make a table

11. Sarah can make 4 sandwiches in 10 minutes. If Sarah needs to make 16 sandwiches for a picnic, how long will it take her?

_____

12. Josh, Kayla and Anthony are volunteering at the pool for the summer. Josh can fold 3 towels in 10 minutes. Kayla can fold 5 towels in 10 minutes, and Anthony can fold 7 towels in 10 minutes. If they all fold towels together, how many towels can they fold in one hour?

_____

Name _____ Date _____

Problem-Solving Practice

4AF2.1

Balanced Equations

The table below shows the price of David's favorite activities.

Activity	Price
skate park	$4
movies	$9
go-carts	$13
pizza dinner	$17
amusement park	$34

1. The sum of going to the skate park and go-carting equals the price of another activity. Write an equation for this situation.

_____

2. David picks a movie and pizza dinner. His friend picks a movie and go-carts. Write an equation for this situation. Tell if it balanced.

_____

The table below shows how many students voted for each activity.

Activity	Number of Votes
kickball	12
pizza lunch	15
extra recess	20
art time	8

3. The difference in votes between extra recess and art time equals the votes for another activity. Write an equation for this situation.

_____

4. One class votes 6 for kickball and 14 for pizza. Another class votes 7 for art time and 11 for extra recess. Write the equation for this situation. Tell whether the equation is balanced.

_____

40

Name _____ Date _____

Homework Practice

4SDAP1.1

Collect and Organize Data

Chapter Resources

Organize the set of data in a tally chart.

1. While Ryan waited for his bus, he watched cars go by and recorded the color of the cars. Here is what he saw.

Color of cars: red, white, blue, white, tan, red, tan, blue, red, tan, blue, white, tan, red, tan, white, tan, tan, white, tan, blue, tan, blue, white, blue, tan

Color of Cars	
Color	**Tally**
Red	
Tan	
White	
Blue	

Organize the set of data in a frequency table.

2. Alyssa records what her friends say is their favorite day of the school week. Place this information in a frequency table.

Day	Votes
Monday	||
Tuesday	||||
Wednesday		
Thursday	ℍℍ|
Friday	ℍℍ ||||

Day	Votes

Spiral Review

Find the missing number in each equation. (Lesson 3–6)

3. $8 + 3 + 9 = 8 +$ _____

6. $16 + 8 = 7 + 9 +$ _____

4. $4 + 16 = 8 + 8 +$ _____

7. $18 + 6 = 5 + 13 +$ _____

5. $9 + 10 = 9 + 6 +$ _____

8. $19 + 5 = 11 + 8 +$ _____

Name _____ Date _____

Problem-Solving Practice

Collect and Organize Data

Solve. Use a separate sheet of paper if necessary.

1. Make a tally chart for the number of students in the third-, fourth-, and fifth-grade classes: 26, 25, 27, 27, 26, 28, 27.

   _____

2. Use the data in your tally chart from Exercise 1. Which class size is most common?

   _____

3. Make a tally chart and a frequency table for the number of books read by students during the summer: 4, 5, 7, 2, 4, 5, 6, 7, 8, 4, 5, 3. How many students took part in this survey?

   _____

4. If another student is added to the survey and says she read 7 books, how would you change your tally chart and frequency table to show this?

   _____

   _____

5. Make a tally chart and a frequency table for the data showing amount of time it takes students to do their homework: 35 min., 1 hour, $1\frac{1}{2}$ hours, 45 min., 60 min., 30 min., 45 min., 90 min., $\frac{1}{2}$ hour. According to your frequency table, what is the longest time it takes the students to do their homework?

   _____

   _____

6. What is the difference between the greatest amount of time and the least amount of time spent doing homework?

   _____

Name _____ Date _____

Homework Practice

Find Mode, Median, and Outliers

Find the mode and median of the set of data. Identify any outliers.

1. Movie ticket prices

Theaters	Plex	Multi	Cine	Matinee	Center	Theater	Main
Price	$8	$9	$9	$9	$8	$7	$6

Mode: _____   Median: _____   Outlier: _____

2. Scores in basketball games

Game	1	2	3	4	5	6	7
Score	45	57	62	59	57	55	60

Mode: _____   Median: _____   Outlier: _____

Spiral Review

Organize the data in a tally chart and a frequency table. (Lesson 4–1)

3. Katherine watched students choose lunch from among four choices. Here is what she saw. Make a tally chart and frequency table of Katherine's data.

Lunch Choices: pizza, salad, taco, pizza, sandwich, salad, taco, taco, pizza, taco, sandwich, taco, salad, pizza, taco, sandwich, salad, taco, pizza, taco, salad, pizza, sandwich, taco, pizza, taco, salad, taco, pizza

Lunch	Tally

Frequency Table:	

Name _____ Date _____

Problem-Solving Practice

Find Mode, Median, and Outliers

Normal Temperatures in January (°F)				
Texas 43	Nebraska 21	Minnesota 12	Michigan 23	Illinois 21
Oklahoma 36	S. Dakota 22	Iowa 19	Indiana 26	Missouri 26
Kansas 25	N. Dakota 9	Wisconsin 20	Ohio 26	Arkansas 39

Use data from the table to solve.

1. Find the **median** and the **mode** of the data.

   _____

   _____

2. What is the difference between the greatest temperature and the least temperature?

   _____

3. Which three states have the same normal temperature in January?

   _____

4. Are there any outliers in this data? Explain.

   _____

   _____

5. Find the median and mode for the five states with the **lowest** temperature.

   _____

6. Find the median and mode for the five states with the **highest** temperature.

   _____

Name _____ Date _____

Homework Practice

Problem-Solving Strategy

Solve. Use the *make a table* strategy.

1. Rosa knits sweaters to sell. Each sweater takes 4 balls of yarn. How many balls of yarn will she need to make 8 sweaters?

   _____

2. Each ball of yarn costs $6. How much money will Rosa earn selling all 28 sweaters if she sells each sweater for $35? Remember, she

   has to pay for the yarn she used to make the sweaters. _____

3. Josh is a photographer. For every 7 pictures he takes, he has one portrait he can sell for $15. If Josh made $180 selling portraits,

   how many photographs did he take? _____

4. Hannah practices her gymnastics routine 12 times at each practice. If she practices 5 days a week, about how many times does

   Hannah practice her routine in 4 weeks? _____

Spiral Review

Find the mode and median of the set of data. Identify any outliers. (Lesson 4-2)

5. Students absent because of the flu

Month	Students
September	25
October	125
November	125
December	175
January	175
February	225
March	175

Mode: _____

Median: _____

Outlier: _____

6. Average travel time to school

Student	Javier	Daniel	Lourdes	Kayla	William	Amber	Kyle
Time	10	15	10	20	10	20	40

Mode: _____

Median: _____

Outlier: _____

Name _____ Date _____

Homework Practice

Line Plots

Organize each set of data in a line plot.

1. Number of books checked out per person at the library.

Number of Books	People
2	3
3	2
4	2
5	1
10	1

2. Number of homeruns hit per game.

Game	Homeruns
1	3
2	2
3	0
4	1
5	3
6	2
7	2

Identify the mode, median, and any outliers for the data set.

3. Number of books checked out per person.

Mode: _____ Median: _____ Outlier: _____

4. Number of homeruns hit per game.

Mode: _____ Median: _____ Outlier: _____

Spiral Review   Solve. (Lesson 4-3)

5. Aaron is selling popcorn to raise money for the band. He sells 1 box of popcorn for every 3 houses he visits. How many houses will he need to visit to sell 9 boxes of popcorn? _____

6. Kimberly babysits 3 hours on weekends. For every 3 hours she works, she earns $25. If she wants to earn $165, how many weekends must she work? _____

7. If Kimberly starts working 5 hours on weekends and earns $42, how many weekends must she work to earn the $165?

Name _____ Date _____

Problem-Solving Practice

Line Plots

Jennifer wants to know how hard her friends thought the extra credit math problem was. She asked them how many tries it took them to solve the problem. She made a chart of her information.

Friends	Answer
Dylan	3
Allison	5
Jose	12
Olivia	4
Jesse	6
Chelsea	4
Logan	6
Maria	7
Trevor	4

1. Organize the data in a line plot.

2. How many tries was the most common answer? _____

3. What was the median number of tries? _____

4. One friend's answer was very different from the other friends. How many tries did the one very different friend take? _____

Hunter wants to know how old his classmates were when they learned how to swim. He took a survey and made a chart of his data:

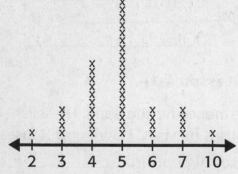

5. What age was the most common age to learn to swim? _____

6. What ages had the same number of students learn to swim?

_____

7. What age was very different from all the other students' ages?

_____

Name _____ Date _____

Homework Practice

Bar and Double Bar Graphs

For Exercises 1–3, use the bar graph below.

This graph shows the number of students using the school gym after school.

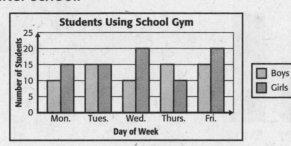

1. Which day had the most number of students using the gym?

_____

2. Did more girls or boys use the gym after school?

_____

3. Estimate how many boys used the gym.

_____

Spiral Review

Organize the set of data in a line plot. (Lesson 4-4)

4. Number of books checked out per person at the library.

Number of Books	People
4	8
6	6
7	6
8	6
19	1

Identify the mode, median, and any outliers for the data set.

5. Number of books checked out per person.

Mode: _____

Median: _____

Outlier: _____

Name _____ Date _____

Problem-Solving Practice

4SDAP1.3

Bar and Double Bar Graphs

For Exercises 1–2, use the bar graph below.

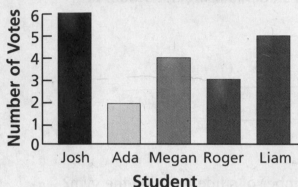

1. How many more votes did Josh get than Roger? Explain how you

know. _____

2. How many votes did Ada and Roger get? Explain how you know.

_____

Use a separate sheet of paper to make a bar graph. Then solve.

3. Maurice made a bar graph to show the number of people wearing
sneakers, boots, and regular shoes in his classroom. Fifteen
students are wearing sneakers. Eight are wearing regular shoes,
and six students are wearing boots. Make a bar graph to show the
data. How many students are in Maurice's class?

_____

4. Betina looked at Maurice's bar graph. She guessed that the
number of students who are wearing regular shoes and boots is
greater than the number of students wearing sneakers. Is Betina's
guess correct? _____

Explain. _____

Name _____   Date _____

Homework Practice

Problem-Solving Investigation

Use any strategy shown below to solve. Tell what strategy you used.

- Draw a picture   • Look for a pattern   • Make a table

1. Each night, Sabrina spends 15 minutes more doing homework than her sister Tiffany. If Tiffany spends 50 minutes in a 5-day week doing homework, how many minutes does Sabrina spend doing homework in that same week? _____

Strategy: _____

2. Caleb is organizing his shirts. He is following a pattern: white, blue, white, red, white, blue… What color is next if this pattern continues? _____

Strategy: _____

3. Corey has 56 people to whom he would like to send a card. If the cards come in packages of 6, how many packages does he need to buy? _____

Strategy: _____

Spiral Review
(Lesson 4–5)

For Exercises 4-6, use the graph shown.

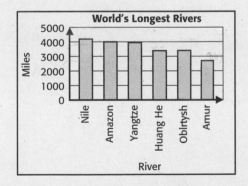

4. Which river is the longest? _____

5. About how long is the Yangtze River? _____

6. Estimate the difference in length between the Nile and the Amur Rivers. _____

Name _____ Date _____

Homework Practice

Interpret Line Graphs

For Exercises 1–5, use the graph that shows the number of students completing their homework.

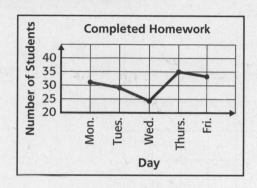

1. On what day did the greatest number of students complete their homework? _____

2. How many students completed their homework on Tuesday? _____

3. On what day did the least number of students complete their homework? _____

4. How many more students completed their homework on Monday than on Wednesday? _____

5. What is the total number of students completing their homework on Tuesday and Friday? _____

Spiral Review   Use any strategy shown below to solve. Tell what strategy you used (Lesson 4–6).

• Look for a Pattern   • Draw a Picture   • Make a Table

6. Emma can borrow tables for her party. Each table can seat 6 guests. If she invites 45 people, how many tables will she need?

_____ Strategy: _____

7. The Pizza Palace sells 2 pizza slices for $3.00, 3 pizza slices for $4.50, and 4 pizza slices for $6.00. At this rate, what is the cost of 1 slice of pizza?_____ Strategy: _____

Name _____ Date _____

Problem-Solving Practice

Interpret Line Graphs

For Exercises 1–2, use the line graph.

Attendance at Drama Club Meetings

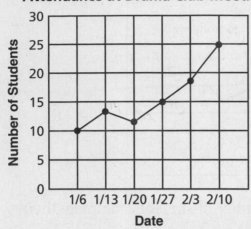

1. Use the line graph to answer this question. What is the greatest number of students at Drama Club meetings? least?

   _____

2. The first meeting on the line graph was the first Monday in January. Did attendance decrease or increase after the beginning of the year?

   _____

Use a separate sheet of paper to make a line graph. Then solve.

Make a line graph of the data. Title it, "Days Jon Practiced Piano."

Month	Days Practiced
July	17
August	15
September	12
October	13
November	12
December	19

3. During which month did Jon practice the greatest number of days? _____

4. During which two months did Jon practice the fewest number of days?

   _____

Name _____ Date _____

Homework Practice

Analyze Graphs

For Exercises 1–4, use the bar graph.

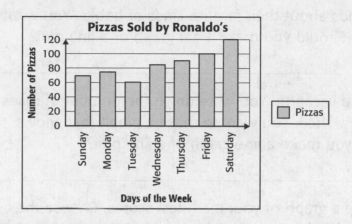

1. Which day did Ronaldo's sell the most pizzas? _____

2. How many pizzas were sold on Thursday? _____

3. What was the total number of pizzas sold on Monday and Tuesday? _____

4. How many more pizzas were sold on Saturday than Wednesday? _____

Spiral Review   **For Exercises 5–8, use the graph. (Lesson 4–7).**

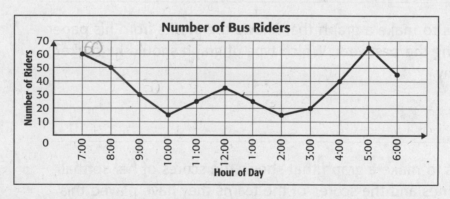

5. Which hour had the greatest number of riders? _____

6. How many people rode the bus at 3:00? _____

7. Which two hours had a combined 125 riders? _____

8. How many more people rode the bus at 7:00 than at 10:00?

_____

Name _____ Date _____

Problem-Solving Practice

Analyze Graphs

Determine the best graph to show the data.

1. You ask your friends about their favorite kinds of books. You want to show the data. Should you make a bar graph or a line plot?

   _____

2. Your family takes a vacation. You write down the number of miles you drive each day. Then, you want to make a graph that shows this data. Should you make a line graph or a line plot?

   _____

3. You want to make a graph of your math test scores. Choose the best type of graph for the data. Explain your choice.

   _____

   _____

4. You want to make a graph that shows the number of times you have ridden your bicycle in the last six weeks. Choose the best type of graph for the data. Explain your choice.

   _____

   _____

5. Julio wants to make a graph that shows the profits from his paper route during the past year. Which type of graph should he make? Explain why.

   _____

   _____

6. Kim wants to make a graph that shows the scores of her softball team's games and the scores of the teams they have played this season. Which is the best type of graph to make for the data? Explain why.

   _____

   _____

   _____

5-1

Homework Practice

Relate Multiplication and Division

4MR2.3, 4NS3.0

Write a fact family for each set of numbers.

1. 3, 6, 18

_____

_____

_____

_____

2. 2, 5, 10

_____

_____

_____

3. $3 \times \boxed{} = 21$ $21 \div 7 = \boxed{}$

$7 \times \boxed{} = 21$ $21 \div 3 = \boxed{}$

Divide. Use a related multiplication fact.

4. $25 \div 5 =$ ___   **6.** $56 \div 8 =$ ___

5. $72 \div 9 =$ ___   **7.** $42 \div 7 =$ ___

Spiral Review

Use the line graph below to answer Exercises 8 and 9.

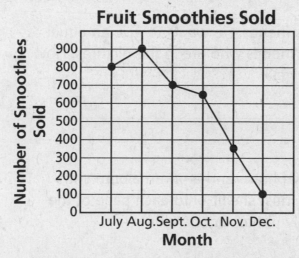

Fruit Smoothies Sold

8. What two months does the Fruit Smoothie Store have the most

business? _____

9. How many more fruit smoothies were sold in September than

in December? _____

Problem-Solving Practice

4MR2.3, 4NS3.0

Relate Multiplication and Division

Solve.

1. Min has 10 photos. She separates them into 2 equal groups. How many photos are in each group?

   _____

2. Kara has 12 photos. She wants to put an equal number of photos on each of 3 pages. How many photos should she put on each page?

   _____

3. Carl took 48 photos on his camping trip. He wants to put an equal number of photos on 8 pages of his photo album. How many photos should he put on each page?

   _____

4. Eduardo has 63 photos of his friends. He wants to give an equal number of photos to 7 of his friends who are in the pictures. How many photos will each friend get?

   _____

5. Helena has a box of 78 family photos and a photo album with 10 pages. How many photos must she fit onto each page of the album to keep all of the family photos in one album?

   _____

Name _____ Date _____

Homework Practice

Algebra: Multiplication and Division Properties

Identify the property shown by each number sentence.

1. $5 \times (2 \times 4) = (5 \times 2) \times 4$

_____

2. $8 \div 8 = 1$ _____

3. $33 \times 1 = 33$

_____

Complete each number sentence. Identify each property shown.

4. $5 \div \boxed{} = 1$ _____

5. $9 \times 8 = 8 \times \boxed{}$

_____

6. $\boxed{} \div 12 = 0$

_____

Spiral Review

Complete each fact family. (Lesson 5-1)

7. $6 \times 5 = \boxed{}$

$5 \times \boxed{} = 30$

$30 \div 5 = \boxed{}$

$30 \div 6 = \boxed{}$

Divide. Use a related multiplication fact.

8. $20 \div 2 =$ _____

9. $72 \div 9 =$ _____

10. $42 \div 7 =$ _____

5-2

Problem-Solving Practice

4AF1.0

Algebra: Multiplication and Division Properties

Solve.

1. Multiply. $3 \times 5 =$ _____

   Then use the Commutative Property to write a different multiplication sentence.

   _____

2. Multiply. $6 \times 8 =$ _____

   Then use the Commutative Property to write a different multiplication sentence.

   _____

3. There are 3 balls in a can of tennis balls. Write a multiplication sentence to show how many balls are in 4 cans.

   _____

4. Karly has 2 model cars that are blue. She has 2 model cars that are red. She has 2 model cars that are silver. Write a multiplication sentence to show how many model cars she has.

   _____

5. Inga has 3 packs with 2 pens in each pack. She has 2 packs with 3 pencils in each pack. Write two multiplication sentences to show how many pens and pencils she has.

   _____

6. Ellie is using beads to make 7 bracelets. She puts 9 beads on 4 of the bracelets. She puts 8 beads on 3 of the bracelets. How many beads does she use?

   _____

Name _____ Date _____

Homework Practice

4NS3.0

Multiply and Divide Facts Through 5

Multiply or divide.

1. 4×4 _____

2. 2×6 _____

3. 5×1 _____

4. 0×7 _____

5. 10×4 _____

6. 2×3 _____

7. 7×2 _____

8. 4×5 _____

9. $3 \div 1$ _____

10. $12 \div 4$ _____

11. $8 \div 2$ _____

12. $15 \div 3$ _____

ALGEBRA Complete each number sentence.

13. $\boxed{} \times 2 = 16$

14. $3 \times 5 = \boxed{}$

15. $\boxed{} \div 5 = 4$

16. $33 \div \boxed{} = 3$

Spiral Review

Complete each number sentence. Identify the property shown. (Lesson 5-2)

17. $5 \times (2 \times 7) = (5 \times \underline{\hspace{1cm}}) \times 7$

_____

18. $\underline{\hspace{1cm}} \div 11 = 0$

_____

19. $8 \times \underline{\hspace{1cm}} = 8$

_____

20. $2 \times 7 = 7 \times \underline{\hspace{1cm}}$

_____

Name _____ Date _____

Problem-Solving Practice

4NS3.0

Multiply and Divide Facts Through 5

Solve.

1. If you have 5 four-wheel trucks, how many total wheels are there?

_____

2. If there are 4 books to a set and you have 5 sets, how many books do you have?

_____

3. There were 4 schools that each had 7 classes attend a seminar. How many total classes were there?

_____

4. There are 3 students on each relay team. How many teams would 15 students make?

_____

5. If 2 boys each make 12 muffins for a bake sale, and there are 2 other people making 12 muffins each, how many total muffins will be for sale?

_____

6. If you have a class of 24 children, how many groups of 4 can you make?

_____

7. If you have a class of 35 students, how many groups of 5 can you make?

_____

8. A teacher gave out 10 stickers a week for 4 weeks. How many stickers did she give away?

_____

Name _____ Date _____

Homework Practice

Problem-Solving Skill

Practice the Strategy

Tell which operation you would use to solve each problem. Then solve.

1. Alejandro works at a soup kitchen each week. He works for 3 hours at a time. How many hours does he work in 12 weeks?

_____

_____

2. There are 4 acrobats in the circus act. If they each have 5 routines, how many routines do they perform altogether?

_____

_____

3. Mario collects baseball cards. If he buys 4 cards a week, how many total cards will he have after 8 weeks?

_____

_____

4. Ann invited 4 friends over to play. They made muffins for a snack. If they made 40 muffins to divide evenly, how many will each

person have? _____

5. Rob bought the three items below. If he paid with three $10 bills,

how much change will he get back? _____

_____

Item	Cost
Swimsuit	$12.95
Goggles	$5.95
Towel	$8.95

Spiral Review   **Multiply or divide. (Lesson 5-3)**

6. 6 × 4 = _____   **8.** 8 × 4 = _____   **10.** 7 × 5 = _____

7. 15 ÷ 5 = _____   **9.** 18 ÷ 3 = _____   **11.** 3 × 4 = _____

Name _____ Date _____

Homework Practice

4MR3.2, 4NS3.0

Multiply and Divide Facts Through 10

Multiply or divide.

1. 8×2 _____

2. $42 \div 7$ _____

3. 7×7 _____

4. $72 \div 8$ _____

5. $6\overline{)60}$ _____

6. $5\overline{)45}$ _____

7. $3\overline{)21}$ _____

8. $100 \div 10$ _____

9. $4\overline{)40}$ _____

10. $50 \div 10$ _____

11.	12.	13.	14.	15.
10	10	5	8	6
$\times 7$	$\times 3$	$\times 4$	$\times 5$	$\times 3$

Spiral Review

Solve. (Lesson 5-4)

16. You buy 3 tickets to a park, but you end up inviting 7 friends to go. Each ticket is good for 2 people. How many more tickets do you need to buy?

_____

17. Jessica downloads 3 songs each week. If she has 24 songs, how many months has she been downloading songs?
(Remember: 4 weeks = 1 month)

_____

18. Look back over this page and circle every number that has a 0 in the ones place. Draw a box around every number with a 4 in the tens place.

5–5

Problem-Solving Practice

Multiply and Divide Facts Through 10

4MR3.2, 4NS3.0

Solve.

1. If you have 8 dogs, how many total legs are there? How many total eyes and ears?

   _____

2. If you have 4 pens to a set and you have 9 sets, how many pens do you have altogether?

   _____

3. There were 4 siblings that each visited the dentist twice a year. How many total times did they visit the dentist in 7 years? 8 years? 10 years?

   _____

4. There are 5 kids on each relay team. How many teams would 35 kids make?

   _____

5. If the boys make 7 toy cars to sell at a fundraiser for $5 each, how much money will they raise?

   _____

6. If you have a belt that is 10 inches long, how long would 7 belts be?

   _____

7. If you have a basket of 9 strawberries, and you pick 5 more baskets with the same amount, how many berries are there altogether?

   _____

8. If you have 8 toy dinosaurs in a box, and you have 5 boxes, how many total toy dinosaurs do you have?

   _____

Name _____ Date _____

Homework Practice

4MR3.3, 4NS3.0

Multiply with 11 and 12

Multiply or divide.

1. 11 × 6 _____   **2.** 12 ÷ 3 _____   **3.** 5)‾5‾5‾ _____

4. 3 × 12 _____   **5.** 44 ÷ 4 _____   **6.** 12)‾6‾0‾ _____

7. 5 × 11 _____   **8.** 99 ÷ 9 _____   **9.** 11)‾8‾8‾ _____

10. 12 × 8 _____   **11.** 96 ÷ 12 _____   **12.** 5)‾6‾0‾ _____

13.   11
        × 5

14.   11
        × 3

15.   12
        × 2

16.   12
        × 9

ALGEBRA Solve.

17. Consuela has 95 people invited to her family reunion. Each table can hold 12 people. How many tables will be needed?

_____

18. Juanita is painting a fence. She is painting 12 boards an hour. How

many hours will it take her to paint 108 boards? _____

 **Review**

Multiply or divide. (Lesson 5-5)

19. 12 ÷ 6 = ____   **21.** 7 × 2 = _____   **23.** 18 ÷ 3 = _____

20. 4 × 5 = _____   **22.** 30 ÷ 6 = ____   **24.** 6 × 4 = _____

5–6

Problem-Solving Practice

4MR3.3, 4NS3.0

Multiply with 11 and 12

Multiply or divide.

1. How many legs do 11 dogs have?

   _____

2. If you have 11 backpacks with 5 books in each one, how many total books are there?

   _____

3. There were 4 math tutors who each had 12 students to tutor in a day. How many students did they see altogether?

   _____

4. You have 11 packs of gum. Each pack has 8 sticks of gum. How many sticks of gum do you have in all?

   _____

5. For every 12 cans you recycle, you receive $0.50. If your family collected 144 cans, how much money would you receive?

   _____

6. If you measure a room that is 11 feet × 12 feet, how many total square feet are there?

   _____

7. If you have a basket of 11 blueberries and you pick 8 more baskets with the same amount, how many berries are there altogether?

   _____

8. You have 12 model cars in a box. If you have 3 boxes, how many total cars do you have?

   _____

Name _____ Date _____

Homework Practice

Problem-Solving Investigation

Solve. Tell the strategy that you used.

1. Jayden has read 22 pages of the newspaper. Adrian has read 42 pages. How many pages have they read altogether?

   _____

2. Sergio was building a model plane. It took 6 days to build the model. If he worked for 4 hours a day, how many total hours did he take to complete the model? What if it took 7 days? 8 days?

   _____

3. If there are 24 pieces of popcorn in a serving, and you eat 72 pieces, how many total servings have you consumed?

   _____

   How many pieces of popcorn will you need for 4 people allowing 1 serving per person?

   _____

4. Catalina, Jose, and Diego went to get a pizza. If they spent $18 altogether and they split the bill evenly, what did they each pay?

   _____

Spiral Review

Multiply or divide. (Lesson 5-6)

5. $60 \div 5 =$ _____

6. $4 \times 11 =$ _____

7. $7 \times 12 =$ _____

8. $24 \div 12 =$ _____

9. $33 \div 3 =$ _____

10. $9 \times 12 =$ _____

11. A school bus can fit 4 passengers in each row. If you have a bus with 12 rows, how many students can fit on it? _____

12. Look back over this page. Circle all the answers on this page that are less than 20.

Name _____ Date _____

Homework Practice

4AF1.0

Multiply Three Numbers

Multiply.

1. $5 \times 2 \times 7$ _____

2. $8 \times 3 \times 2$ _____

3. $4 \times 2 \times 5$ _____

4. $5 \times 3 \times 4$ _____

5. $6 \times 3 \times 1$ _____

6. $4 \times 2 \times 4$ _____

7. $7 \times 2 \times 6$ _____

8. $9 \times 4 \times 2$ _____

9. $10 \times 12 \times 1$ _____

10. $6 \times 2 \times 5$ _____

11. $5 \times 4 \times 2$ _____

12. $0 \times 12 \times 1$ _____

ALGEBRA Copy and complete each number sentence.

13. $4 \times \blacksquare \times 8 = 64$ _____

14. $2 \times 4 \times \blacksquare = 80$ _____

15. $4 \times \blacksquare \times 5 = 60$ _____

16. $3 \times 3 \times \blacksquare = 72$ _____

17. $5 \times 3 \times 4 = \blacksquare$ _____

18. $10 \times 11 \times \blacksquare = 0$ _____

19. $5 \times 1 \times 4 = \blacksquare$ _____

20. $10 \times 5 \times \blacksquare = 100$ _____

21. If you walk 3 miles a day 3 days a week, how many miles will you

walk in 9 weeks? _____

Spiral Review

Use the make a table strategy or choose an operation to solve each problem. (Lesson 5-7)

22. Donas earned 267 points on the first level of a video game. He earned 38 more points on the second level than the first. How many total points did Donas earn after two levels?

_____

23. A boat can fit 2 passengers in each row. How many people can fit in a boat with 8 rows? _____

24. If you and 3 friends go to a movie and pay $36 for your tickets, how much do you each pay? _____

Name _____ Date _____

Problem-Solving Practice

Multiply Three Numbers

Multiply.

1. If you have a pet snake that eats 2 times a week, how many times will you feed it in 6 weeks? _____

2. A teacher wants to buy 4 new basketballs for each class in 2 schools. Each school has 4 elementary classes and 5 middle-school classes. How many basketballs does the teacher need to buy? _____

3. Jose rides 5 miles on his bike one way to school. How many miles will he ride in 10 days to and from school? _____

4. If 8 people fit in a row on an airplane, and there are 12 rows, how many people would fit into the plane? _____

5. A boat can carry 6 people and allows 2 suitcases per person. How many suitcases can 4 boats hold?

_____

6. If you and 6 friends go on a roller coaster ride 5 times, and it is $2 per person per ride, what is the total price you pay for rides?

_____

How much would you spend if you went on a roller coaster 6 times with the same group of friends for the same price? _____

Name _____ Date _____

Homework Practice

Factors and Multiples

Find all of the **factors** of each number.

1. 2 _____

4. 20 _____

2. 4 _____

5. 33 _____

3. 14 _____

6. 37 _____

Identify the first five **multiples** for each number.

7. 2 ___, ___, ___, ___, ____

8. 3 ___, ___, ___, ____, ____

9. 6 ___, ____, ____, ____, ____

10. 8 ___, ____, ____, ____, ____

11.

If you eat 1 banana each day, how many bananas will you eat in 12 days? In 10, 11, and 13 days? _____, _____, _____, _____

Spiral Review

Multiply. (Lesson 5–8)

12. $4 \times 1 \times 3$

____

14. $5 \times 2 \times 4$

____

13. $3 \times 2 \times 12$

____

15. $5 \times 1 \times 12$

____

Name _____ Date _____

Problem-Solving Practice

Factors and Multiples

Solve.

1. 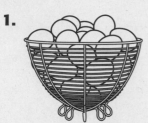 If you eat 2 eggs each day, how many eggs will you eat in 6 days? In 7, 8, and 9 days?

   _____, _____, _____, _____

2. A bird eats 7 berries a day. How many berries does it eat in 4 days? 5 days? 1 week?

   _____, _____, _____

3. A golf cart with two rows can carry 2 passengers in each row. If you have 6 carts, how many people can fit in them?

   _____

4. If you and a friend go to the park and pay $18 to rent bicycles, how much do you each owe? _____

5. Ramon is organizing the desks in his classroom. He wants them in straight rows and columns. How many ways can he organize the 15 desks in the classroom? List the factors.

   _____

   How many ways can he organize 32 desks? List the factors.

   _____

   How many ways can he organize 27 desks? List the factors.

   _____

6. A pet store has 4 dogs for sale. They have three times as many fish for sale, twice as many birds for sale, and half as many cats for sale. How many total animals are for sale? _____

Name _____ Date _____

Homework Practice

Prime and Composite Numbers

Find the factors of each number. Then tell whether the number is *prime, composite,* or *neither.*

1. 3 _____

2. 7 _____

3. 12 _____

Solve.

4. Arrange 6 model race cars. You want to order them in equal rows and columns. How many ways can you arrange them? _____

_____

5. List the factors for 3, 9, and 18. _____

_____

_____

 **Spiral Review**

Find all of the factors of each number. (Lesson 5–9)

6. 8 _____

7. 24 _____

Identify the first five multiples for each number.

8. 7 _____

9. 5 _____

Problem-Solving Practice

4NS4.2

Prime and Composite Numbers

Solve.

1. Arrange books on your desk so that 4 books are in equal rows. Decide if 4 is a prime or composite number. If it is a composite number, list all the ways to present the books.

   _____

   _____

2. You decide you are going to arrange 8 pictures hanging on the wall. You want them in equal rows and columns. How many ways can you arrange them? _____

   _____

3. There are 18 members in a dance class and they are performing in a parade. How many ways can they dance if the rows and columns are equal? _____

4. If you are making a quilt with square fabric pieces, and you are making equal rows and columns, list the ways you can use 48 pieces. _____

5. Isabel is organizing a section of the classroom library. Is there any way that she can organize the 31 books with cassettes equally? Why or why not?

   _____

   _____

6. How many ways can you organize your 40 toys on a series of shelves with equal rows and columns?

   _____

Name _____ Date _____

Homework Practice

Multiplication and Division Expressions

Find the value of each expression if $j = 12$ and $k = 6$.

1. $j \div 3$ _____   **2.** $k \div 2$ _____   **3.** $3 \times j$ _____

4. $5 \times k$ _____   **5.** $j \times k$ _____   **6.** $j \div k$ _____

7. $5 \times (j \div 4)$ _____   **8.** $(18 \div k) \div 3$ _____   **9.** $(j \div k) \times 5$ _____

Write an expression for each situation.

10. a number multiplied by 3 _____

11. the product of 5 and a number _____

12. 16 divided by a number _____

13. a number divided by 8 _____

14. Three times a week, Savannah does yard work for her neighbors for 2 hours. If she is paid $5 per hour, how much does she earn each week? Write an expression using m for money and solve.

_____

Spiral Review   Identify the factors of each number.
Decide whether the number is composite or prime. (Lesson 5–10)

15. 4 _____

16. 7 _____

17. 18 _____

18. 29 _____

19. 36 _____

20. 41 _____

21. Mrs. Hernandez is hanging 17 posters in the gym. Is there any way she can arrange the posters so that they are in even rows? Tell whether 17 is a composite or prime number. Explain.

_____

_____

Name _____ Date _____

Problem-Solving Practice

Multiplication and Division Expressions

Solve.

1. Ming and Amy have 6 bags of beads. Each bag contains 14 beads. Define a variable and write an expression for the number of beads Ming and Amy have. Then find the total number of beads.

   _____

2. If Ming buys 3 more bags of beads, how many beads will Ming and Amy have altogether?

   _____

3. Julie's mother is 40 years old. She is 4 times as old as Julie. To find Julie's age, solve the equation $40 \div a = 4$, where a equals Julie's age.

   _____

4. Andrew has three boxes of holiday decorations. There are 12 decorations in each box. Write and solve an expression for the number of decorations in each box. Then solve the expression.

   _____

5. George and his brother have a total of 8 CDs. Each CD has the same amount of songs. If there are 88 total songs, how many songs are on each CD? Write an expression to find the number of songs on each CD. Then solve the expression.

   _____

6. Each of Mrs. Fairview's children needs 3 books for school. She has 4 children. If each book costs $8, what will be the total cost for all of the books? Write an expression to find the total amount the books will cost. Then solve the expression.

   _____

Name _____ Date _____

Homework Practice

Problem-Solving Strategy

Solve. Use the *work backward* strategy.

1. Paige gave 12 barrettes to her sister. Jordan gave Paige 5 more barrettes. Then Paige gave 6 barrettes to Maria. Now Paige has 8 barrettes. How many barrettes did Paige have to start with?

_____

2. Luis bought 6 new baseball cards on Tuesday. On Thursday he bought three times as many. He now has 35 baseball cards. How

many cards did he have originally? _____

3. Mary practiced playing the piano twice as long Monday than Tuesday. Tuesday she practiced 20 minutes less than Wednesday. Wednesday she practiced for 30 minutes. How long did Mary practice playing

the piano on Monday? _____

4. In Jared's school, 6 more fourth-graders use blue pens than black. Four times as many fourth-graders use pencils than blue pens. If 5 fourth-graders use black pens, how many fourth-graders use

pencils? _____

Spiral Review Find the value of each expression if $q = 15$ and $r = 5$. (Lesson 6-1)

5. $q \div 5$ _____

6. $4 \times r$ _____

7. $5 \times (q \div 5)$ _____

8. $(20 \div r) \div 2$ _____

Write an expression for each situation.

9. 6 multiplied by a number _____

10. a number divided by 5 _____

11. Each of three friends can decorate 3 pencil boxes a day. Write an expression to show how many pencil boxes the friends can decorate in d days.

_____

_____

Name _____ Date _____

Homework Practice

Order of Operations

Find the value of each expression.

1. $(3 + 2) \times 5$ _____

2. $(13 - 5) \div 4$ _____

3. $7 \times (12 - 9)$ _____

4. $18 \div (4 + 5)$ _____

5. $(24 \div 8) + (5 \times 6)$ _____

6. $(8 \times 6) - (25 - 7)$ _____

7. $4 \times 3 - 7$ _____

8. $8 - 9 \div 3$ _____

9. $6 \div 3 + 8$ _____

10. $15 - 3 \times 3$ _____

11. $2 \times 4 + 5 - 6$ _____

12. $21 \div 7 + 8 - 5$ _____

13. Juan collects shells. He had 15 before he went on vacation. On vacation he found 4 shells per day for 3 days. Then he found 6 shells on the fourth day. Write an expression and solve it to find out how many shells he has after vacation.

_____

14. Michelle practices dribbling the soccer ball for 10 minutes each day during the school week. She practices for 30 minutes each day on the weekend. How many minutes does she practice during a whole week?

_____

Spiral Review   Solve. Use the work *backward* strategy. (Lesson 6-2)

15. Hunter gave his sister $3. He earned $12. Then he paid $6 for lunch. Now Hunter has $18. How much money did Hunter have to start with? _____

16. Mark downloaded 8 new songs on Tuesday. On Thursday he downloaded four times as many. He now has 45 songs. How many songs did he have originally? _____

Name _____ Date _____

Problem-Solving Practice

4AF1.3

Order of Operations

Write which operation should be done first. Then solve.

1. Tod buys 4 packs of batteries. Each pack has 4 batteries. He gives 6 batteries to his sister. How many batteries does he have left?

   $4 \times 4 - 6 =$ _____ batteries

   Which operation should be done first? _____

2. Ryan has 36 stickers. He buys 6 more stickers. Then he divides the stickers into 6 groups. How many stickers are in each group?

   $(36 + 6) \div 6 =$ _____ stickers

   Which operation should be done first?

   _____

Use the proper order of operations to solve.

3. Jen had 6 blank CDs, but needed to buy more. She bought 2 packs of blank CDs. Each pack has 8 CDs. How many blank CDs does she have now?

   $6 + 2 \times 8 =$ _____ CDs

4. Sara has 20 stickers. She buys 5 packs of stickers. Each pack has 8 stickers. She adds the stickers to her collection. How many stickers does she have in her collection now?

   $20 + 5 \times 8 =$ _____ stickers

Solve.

5. Coach Coleman has 32 softballs left from last season, but 3 are torn and cannot be used. He buys 2 boxes of softballs to start the new season. Each box has 12 softballs. How many good softballs does he have in all? Show your work.

   _____

6. Coach Coleman is ordering hats for this year's teams. There are 6 teams. Each team has 12 players on the roster. He orders 12 more hats for the team managers. How many hats does he order in all? Show your work.

Name _____ Date _____

Homework Practice

Solve Equations Mentally

Solve each equation mentally.

1. $5 \times q = 45$ _____

2. $h \times 4 = 32$ _____

3. $6 \times u = 36$ _____

4. $5 \times r = 60$ _____

5. $11 \times c = 77$ _____

6. $56 \div j = 7$ _____

7. $y \div 8 = 9$ _____

8. $k \div 7 = 5$ _____

9. $27 \div d = 9$ _____

Write an equation for each situation. Then solve.

10. A number multiplied by 9 equals 36. What is the number?

_____

11. 8 times a number equals 48. What is the number?

_____

12. A number divided by 7 equals 4. What is the number?

_____

13. 132 divided by a number equals 11. What is the number?

_____

14. Devin has saved twice as much money as Gabrielle. Devin has saved $20. Write and solve a multiplication equation to find how much

Gabrielle has saved. _____

15. Mark takes 4 times as long to get to school as Alicia. Mark takes 28 minutes to get to school. Write and solve an equation to find

how long it takes Alicia to get to school. _____

Spiral Review Find the value of each expression. (Lesson 6-3)

16. $(4 + 3) \times 6$ _____

17. $(12 - 8) \div 2$ _____

18. $(7 \times 3) - (23 - 7)$ _____

19. $5 \times 2 - 6$ _____

20. $7 - 18 \div 3$ _____

21. $16 \div 4 + 7 - 2$ _____

22. Miguel found T-shirts for $6 each. His mother bought him 5 shirts. Then she used a coupon for $7 off the total price. Write an expression and solve it to find how much the 5 T-shirts cost.

_____

6-4

Problem-Solving Practice

Solve Equations Mentally

Write an equation for each situation. Then solve.

1. Mrs. Jones needs to say how many people, including chaperones, will be on the school trip. Each of the 4 fourth-grade classrooms is sending 11 students. The school is sending 5 chaperones. Write and solve an equation to find how many total people are going on the school trip. _____

_____

2. Nathan went hiking for 2 hours with his older brother. He covered *n* miles at a speed of 4 miles each hour. Write and solve an equation to find how many miles Nathan hiked. _____

_____

3. Tiffany can hold her breath 5 times longer than Marcus can. Tiffany held her breath for 60 seconds. Write and solve an equation to find how long Marcus held his breath. _____

_____

4. Four friends went apple picking. Each friend picked the same number of apples. The whole group picked a total of 44 apples. Write and solve an equation to find how many apples each friend picked. _____

_____

5. Ricardo has 5 times as many perfect papers in math as Sean does. Sean has 7 perfect papers. Write and solve an equation to find how many perfect papers Ricardo has. _____

_____

6. Cheyenne baked 48 cookies. It is enough for a number of friends to have 4 cookies each. Write and solve an equation to find how many friends can have cookies. _____

_____

Name _____ Date _____

Homework Practice

Problem-Solving Investigation

Use any strategy below to solve. Tell what strategy you used.

Problem-Solving Strategies

- Make a table
- Choose an operation
- Work backward

1. Christina and her 3 friends want to play mini golf. It costs $4 per person per round of golf. The friends all play 3 rounds of golf. How much change will the friends get back if they pay with $50? _____

   Strategy: _____

2. A playground has three times as many swings as monkey bars. There are 4 more monkey bars than slides. There are 3 slides at the playground. How many swings are at the playground?

   _____

   Strategy: _____

3. Carlos gets to choose the family dinner 3 times for every week that he completes his homework each night. There are 4 weeks each month and 9 months in the school year. How many times could Carlos get to choose the dinner? _____

   Strategy: _____

Spiral Review

Solve each equation mentally. (Lesson 6-4)

4. $6 \times q = 48$ _____

5. $h \times 3 = 27$ _____

6. $7 \times u = 42$ _____

7. $6 \times r = 72$ _____

8. $11 \times c = 77$ _____

9. $56 \div j = 8$ _____

10. $y \div 9 = 9$ _____

11. $k \div 4 = 8$ _____

12. $24 \div d = 8$ _____

Name _____ Date _____

Homework Practice

Algebra: Find a Rule

Write an equation that describes the pattern. Then use the equation to find the next three numbers.

1.

Rule: _____	
Input (*v*)	Output (*w*)
8	4
12	6
16	
20	
24	

2.

Rule: _____	
Input (*x*)	Output (*y*)
5	15
6	18
7	
8	
9	

3. Shannon found out there are four yellow pencils for every one blue pencil. Make a table to find how many yellow pencils there would be if she found 4, 6, 8, 10, and 12 blue pencils.

Rule: _____	
Blue Pencils Input (*x*)	Yellow Pencils Output (*y*)

Spiral Review
Use any strategy to solve. Tell what strategy you used. (Lesson 6-5)

4. In Alexa's neighborhood, there are 3 times as many dogs as birds. There are 5 more cats than birds. There are 24 cats. How many

dogs are there? _____ Strategy:

_____

6–6

Problem-Solving Practice

4AF1.5

Algebra: Find a Rule

Jorge and his dad make sandwiches for a party. The table shows grilled cheese and turkey sandwiches.

Rule: _____	
Grilled Cheese Input (c)	Turkey Output (t)
4	1
12	3
20	5
28	
36	

1. Write an equation that describes the relationship between grilled cheese and turkey sandwiches.

   _____

2. How many turkey sandwiches will Jorge make if he is making 28 grilled cheese sandwiches? _____

Chloe is helping plan the class field trip. Her teacher asked her to figure out how many students can come. The table shows the students and chaperones for the field trip.

Rule: _____	
Chaperones Input (c)	Students Output (s)
3	18
5	30
7	42
9	
11	

3. Write an equation that describes the relationship between chaperones and students. _____

4. How many students can come if 9 chaperones go on the field trip?

   _____

5. How many people in all will go if 66 students go on the trip?

_____

Name _____ Date _____

Homework Practice

Balanced Equations

Tell whether each equation is balanced. Explain.

1. $4 \times 4 = 2 \times 2 \times 4$ _____

2. $4 \times 6 \div 8 = (8 \times 2) \div 8$ _____

3. $8 \times 3 \times 2 = 6 \times 4 \times 2$ _____

4. $48 \div 4 = (8 \times 3) \div 2$ _____

Complete each equation to make it balanced.

5. $4 \times (7 - 3) =$ _____ $\times 2$

6. _____ $\div (8 - 5) = (3 - 2) \times 4$

7. Megan scores 5 baskets every quarter. Alexis scores 3 baskets every quarter. Megan played 6 quarters this week. Use the equation $5 \times 6 = 3 \times q$ to find how many quarters Alexis must play to score the same number of baskets. _____

Spiral Review

Write a rule as an equation for the pattern in each table. Then find the next two numbers in each pattern. (Lesson 6-6)

8.

Rule: _____	
Input (*a*)	Output (*b*)
3	1
6	2
9	3
12	
15	

9.

Rule: _____	
Input (*c*)	Output (*d*)
3	12
6	24
9	36
12	
15	

Name _____ Date _____

Problem-Solving Practice

Balanced Equations

Michael and Jessica are going shopping.

Item	Cost
Apple	$1
Milk	$3
Pizza	$6
Chicken Meal	$12

1. Jessica's bill is $35. How many milks did she buy?
   Chicken meal + Pizza + Milk + Apple

   $12 + (2 \times \$6) + (m \times \$3) + (2 \times \$1)$ _____

2. Michael's bill is $49. How many pizzas did he buy?
   Chicken meal + Pizza + Milk + Apple

   $(1 \times \$12) + (p \times \$6) + (5 \times \$3) + (4 \times \$1)$ _____

3. Michael and Jessica want to spend the same amount
   of money. What can Jessica buy to equal Michael's bill?

   _____

Hannah does certain activities at different speeds.

Activity	Speed
jogging	5 mph
walking	3 mph
hiking	2 mph
bicycling	6 mph

4. If Hannah walks 1 hour one day and rides her bike 2 hours
   another day, did she travel the same distance? Explain.

   _____

5. Hannah jogged for 1 hour. On her way back, she walked and
   hiked. If Hannah walked for 1 hour, for how long did she hike?

   _____

Name _____ Date _____

Homework Practice

Multiples of 10, 100, and 1,000

Multiply. Use basic facts and patterns.

1. $4 \times 1 =$ _____

   $4 \times 10 =$ _____

   $4 \times 100 =$ _____

   $4 \times 1,000 =$ _____

2. $6 \times 7 =$ _____

   $6 \times 70 =$ _____

   $6 \times 700 =$ _____

   $6 \times 7,000 =$ _____

Multiply. Use mental math.

3. $2 \times 70 =$ _____

4. $9 \times 500 =$ _____

5. $7 \times 4,000 =$ _____

ALGEBRA Find the value of each variable.

6. $30 \times n = 120$ _____

7. $6 \times n = 3,600$ _____

ALGEBRA Find the value of each expression if $k = 2$.

8. $20 \times k =$ _____

9. $k \times 500 =$ _____

10. Joe bought a house. His payments are $1,000 a month. How much

will he pay for 5 months? _____

Spiral Review

Tell whether each equation is balanced. Explain. (Lesson 6–7)

11. $48 \div 8 = (4 \times 3) \div 2$

_____

12. $6 \times 5 \times 2 = 2 \times 7 \times 3$

_____

_____

13. $3 \times 9 \times 2 = 6 \times 3 \times 3$

_____

Complete each equation to make it balanced.

14. $(16 - 4) \times$ _____ $= 3 \times 8$

15. $3 \times (10 - 3) =$ _____ $\times 7$

Name _____ Date _____

Problem-Solving Practice

Multiples of 10, 100, and 1,000

Solve.

1. There were 20 pirates on a ship. Each one had 1 eye patch. How many eye patches were on the ship in all?

   _____

2. The pirates had 6 treasure chests with gold coins. Each chest had 9,000 gold coins. How many gold coins did the pirates have in all?

   _____

3. The pirates traveled 50 miles every day. They have been at sea for 8 days. How many miles have they traveled altogether?

   _____

4. One day the pirates sighted 2 whales every hour for 10 hours. How many total whales were sighted?

   _____

5. Over the 8 days that they have been at sea, the pirates ate 20 fish each day. How many fish were eaten in all?

   _____

6. The pirates plan to explore 3 islands which will require walking 20 miles per day. How many miles will they have walked if it takes 4 days to explore all 3 islands?

   _____

7. Four of the pirates have been away at sea for 200 days. How many days total have these four pirates been away at sea?

   _____

7-2

Homework Practice

4MR3.1, 4NS3.0

Problem–Solving Skill: Reasonable Answers

Decide whether each answer is reasonable. Explain your reasoning.

1. Sam travels from Baltimore to Boston each year. It takes him 10 hours to get to Boston. He stops 3 times, for an hour each time. If he only stopped once, is it reasonable to say that he could get there in 6 hours? _____

2. The table below shows Sam's expenses for his trip to Boston. Was it reasonable for Sam to say that the trip cost him close to $400?

_____

Expenses	Amount Spent
Food	$103
Gas	$252
Tolls	$36

3. Write a problem that would have $1,000 as a reasonable answer.

_____

_____

Spiral Review   Multiply. Use mental math. (Lesson 7–1)

4. $2 \times 4,000 =$ _____

5. $3 \times 80 =$ _____

6. $9 \times 600 =$ _____

7. $4 \times 5,000 =$ _____

8. $5 \times 50 =$ _____

9. $6 \times 900 =$ _____

10. $6 \times 200 =$ _____

11. $8 \times 1,000 =$ _____

12. $9 \times 30 =$ _____

13. $5 \times 70 =$ _____

ALGEBRA Find the value of each variable.

14. $n \times 20 = 60$ _____

15. $t \times 8 = 56,000$ _____

Name _____ Date _____

Homework Practice

Use Rounding to Estimate Products

Estimate each product.

1. 2 × 36 = _____

2. 96 × 3 = _____

3. 6 × 28 = _____

4. 68 × 4 = _____

5. 5 × 41 = _____

6. 5 × 423 = _____

7. 6 × 523 = _____

8. 3 × 667 = _____

9. 2 × 366 = _____

10. 4 × 712 = _____

Solve.

11. An airline pilot travels about 6,457 miles a week. About how many miles would she travel in a month?

_____

12. If the L.A. Dodgers win about 21 games a month, about how many games would they win after three months?

_____

Spiral Review

Decide whether each answer is reasonable. Explain your reasoning. (Lesson 7-2)

13. Ted Williams had about 30 home runs a season. Is it reasonable to say that he had 300 home runs within a 6-year period?

_____

14. Roger Clemens pitched about 16 winning games per year. After he had played 8 years for the Boston Red Sox, is it reasonable to say that he had about 130 wins?

_____

7-3

Problem-Solving Practice

4NS3.0, 4NS1.3

Use Rounding to Estimate Products

Estimate each product.

1. Each fourth-grade class has 28 students. There are three classes in the school. About how many fourth-grade students are there in all?

   _____

2. Pizzas cost $11 each. Miss Adams buys 4 pizzas. About how much does she spend on pizzas?

   _____

3. Chad's family wants to buy 6 different board games. Each board game costs $17.99. About how much will all of the board games cost?

   _____

4. Habib buys 3 books that cost $9 each. About how much money does he spend on books?

   _____

5. Mr. Bell buys 4 shirts that cost $17 each. He has $50 to spend. Does he have enough money? Explain.

   _____

   _____

Name _____ Date _____

Homework Practice

Multiply Two-Digit Numbers

Multiply.

1. $73 \times 3 =$ _____   2. $88 \times 4 =$ _____

3. $44 \times 5 =$ _____   4. $74 \times 5 =$ _____

5. $31 \times 7 =$ _____   6. $85 \times 4 =$ _____

7. $68 \times 8 =$ _____   8. $77 \times 6 =$ _____

9. $32 \times 9 =$ _____   10. $97 \times 2 =$ _____

11. $65 \times 5 =$ _____   12. $66 \times 8 =$ _____

13. $33 \times 6 =$ _____   14. $94 \times 3 =$ _____

15. $96 \times 3 =$ _____   16. $59 \times 7 =$ _____

Solve.

17. A rectangle is 5 tiles wide by 13 tiles high. How many tiles are in the rectangle?

_____

18. Books are stacked in 3 stacks with 17 books in each stack. How many books are in the stacks?

_____

Spiral Review

Estimate each product. (Lesson 7-3)

19. $89 \times 2 =$ _____   20. $396 \times 4 =$ _____

21. $6 \times 105 =$ _____   22. $3 \times 412 =$ _____

23. $4 \times 209 =$ _____   24. $3 \times 970 =$ _____

Solve.

25. A football player runs about 104 yards each game. After he has played 2 games, *about* how many yards has he run?

_____

Name _____ Date _____

Problem-Solving Practice

Multiply Two-Digit Numbers

Solve.

1. There are 3 birds on the ground. Each bird eats 10 worms. How many worms are eaten all together?

   _____

2. Simon has 12 CDs. He burns 3 copies of each. How many CDs did Simon make?

   _____

3. The school auditorium has 4 rows of seats. There are 18 seats in each row. How many students can sit in the auditorium?

   _____

4. The school cafeteria has 6 rows of tables. Each row has 22 places to sit. How many students can eat in the school cafeteria?

   _____

5. Scott is playing a game of memory with some picture cards. He makes 4 rows and puts 23 cards in each row. How many picture cards is Scott using in this game?

   _____

6. Kate would like to play the memory game, too. She adds her cards to the game. Now, there are 8 rows, and 24 cards in each row. How many cards are there now?

   _____

7. John wants to buy birthday gifts for 8 friends. He can spend $19 for each gift. How much will he spend in all?

   _____

8. Caroline makes $5 an hour pet-sitting for the neighbors. Last summer she worked 31 hours. How much money did Caroline earn?

   _____

Name _____ Date _____

Homework Practice

Problem-Solving Investigation

Use any strategy to solve.

1. Joe has 5 new notebooks for school. Two of those notebooks have 3 sections and three have 5 sections. Joe needs 20 sections in all.

   Does he have enough? _____

2. Each class uses 1,000 sheets of paper every week. The school uses a total of 9,000 sheets of paper every week. How many classes are

   in the school? _____

3. Write a problem that you can solve by looking for a pattern. Explain the pattern you used.

   _____

   _____

   _____

   _____

   _____

Spiral Review

Multiply. (Lesson 7–4)

4. $55 \times 5 =$ _____

5. $75 \times 6 =$ _____

6. $8 \times 47 =$ _____

7. $6 \times 39 =$ _____

8. $2 \times 98 =$ _____

9. $84 \times 6 =$ _____

10. $4 \times 52 =$ _____

11. $63 \times 7 =$ _____

12. $29 \times 9 =$ _____

13. $32 \times 5 =$ _____

14. $4 \times 60 =$ _____

15. $66 \times 8 =$ _____

16. $9 \times 22 =$ _____

17. $72 \times 8 =$ _____

18. $33 \times 5 =$ _____

19. $2 \times 90 =$ _____

Solve.

20. There are 26 teams in the basketball league. Each team has 9 players on its roster. How many players are there all together?

   _____

Name _____ Date _____

Homework Practice

Multiply Multi–Digit Numbers

Multiply.

1. $416 \times 6 =$ _____

2. $293 \times 5 =$ _____

3. $153 \times 4 =$ _____

4. $310 \times 3 =$ _____

5. $2,135 \times 4 =$ _____

6. $5,216 \times 6 =$ _____

7. $\$3,591 \times 3 =$ _____

8. $\$4,325 \times 9 =$ _____

9. $2,135 \times 2 =$ _____

10. $5,112 \times 4 =$ _____

ALGEBRA Find the value of each expression if $n = 3$.

11. $n \times 6,421 =$ _____

12. $n \times 1,913 =$ _____

Solve.

13. There are 9 children in the scout troop. Each of them contributed 127 hours to community clean-up projects. What is the total number of hours the scout troop contributed?

_____

14. Five people donated to the school library this year. Each person donated $225. How much money did the library get in donations this year? _____

Spiral Review

Use any strategy to solve. (Lesson 7-5)

15. For the past 6 weeks, fourth-grade safety guards have worked after school and waited with first-grade students until their parents came for them. The first week they waited with 5 first-graders, the second week with 7, the third week with 9. If the pattern continued, how many first-graders did they wait with for the fourth, fifth, and sixth weeks? _____

16. Twenty babysitters in the babysitters club earned a total of $400 for the club each month. How much would 40 babysitters earn?

_____

Name _____ Date _____

Problem-Solving Practice

Multiply Multi–Digit Numbers

Solve.

1. The first floor of an apartment building has space for 112 small apartments. The next 5 floors are the same. The first 6 floors of the apartment building have space for how many apartments?

_____

2. Each year 6,578 people eat lunch in a certain restaurant. During a period of 5 years, how many people will eat in this restaurant?

_____

3. The maximum number of people that can be on the top of a building at one time is 400. By 10 A.M. one morning there had already been 4 groups of 398 people to the top. How many people have been to the top of the building already?

_____

4. In one greenhouse, there were 427 plants. If there were 5 greenhouses growing the same number of plants, how many plants would there be altogether?

_____

5. A famous concert hall seats 9,551 people. Every seat was filled for the 9 concerts that took place in June. How many people heard a concert in this concert hall in June?

_____

6. A taxi driver kept track of how many people were friendly to him in a day. Sixteen people told him what they were doing in the city, 8 asked him if he had a family, 23 told him what they liked best about the city, and 3 asked if they could buy him coffee. The taxi driver wanted his friends to believe that people are friendly, so he tripled his numbers. How many people did the taxi driver say were friendly to him?

_____

Name _____ Date _____

Homework Practice

Multiply Across Zeros

Multiply.

1. 460 × 6 = _____

2. 308 × 8 = _____

3. 6,404 × 3 = _____

4. 5,060 × 5 = _____

5. 7,032 × 4 = _____

6. 3,056 × 6 = _____

7. 7,501 × 4 = _____

8. 7,810 × 8 = _____

9. $2,058 × 3 = _____

10. $8,040 × 2 = _____

For exercise 11, complete the table.

11. Multiply by 5,809.

Input	5	6	7	8	9
Output					

Solve.

12. Jaime has 8 boxes of beads. Each box has 50 beads in it. How

many beads does she have in all? _____

Spiral Review

Solve (Lesson 7-6)

13. 9,732 × 9 = _____

14. 2,581 × 2 = _____

15. There are 182 bulletin boards throughout the school. Each bulletin
board is covered by 8 large pieces of colored paper. Every summer
the colored paper is replaced. How many sheets of paper does it

take to cover the bulletin boards? _____

16. The school bulletin boards display at least 1,000 students' papers.
The bulletin boards are changed 9 times during the school year. At

least how many student papers are displayed over the year? _____

Name _____ Date _____

Problem-Solving Practice

Multiply Across Zeros

4NS3.0, 4MR2.1

Solve.

1. The school has 206 boxes of chalk. Each box has 8 pieces of chalk inside. How many pieces of chalk are there in all?

   _____

2. There are 401 windows in the school. Each window has 9 panes. When Mr. Parker washes each window pane by hand, how many panes does he wash?

   _____

3. The art teacher ordered 201 sets of markers for her students to use. Each set has 32 markers. How many markers did she order in all?

   _____

4. Each time the art class paints pictures, 108 brushes must be cleaned. If the art class paints pictures 9 times during the year, how many brushes will be cleaned?

   _____

5. Brent rode his bicycle 4 miles during the last day of August. His bicycle has an odometer that measures how far in miles and yards. Each mile has 1,760 yards. How many yards did Brent ride on the last day of August?

   _____

6. Cassandra ran 7 miles during the week. She wears a pedometer that measures how far she runs in miles and yards. Each mile has 1,760 yards. How many yards did Cassandra run in the week?

   _____

Name _____ Date _____

Homework Practice

Multiply by Tens

Multiply.

1. $51 \times 30 =$ _____

2. $712 \times 30 =$ _____

3. $39 \times 80 =$ _____

4. $116 \times 10 =$ _____

5. $67 \times 20 =$ _____

6. $185 \times 80 =$ _____

7. $325 \times 60 =$ _____

8. $490 \times 90 =$ _____

9. $608 \times 40 =$ _____

10. $111 \times 70 =$ _____

11. $999 \times 10 =$ _____

12. $740 \times 50 =$ _____

Solve.

13. There are 40 rows of lockers. There are 12 lockers in each row.

How many lockers are there? _____

14. Pablo found out that every classroom has 34 desks. There are

30 classrooms. How many desks are in the school? _____

 Spiral Review

Multiply. (Lesson 7–7)

15. $604 \times 3 =$ _____

16. $6,005 \times 8 =$ _____

17. $3,100 \times 9 =$ _____

Solve.

18. Mr. Sims printed 303 museum trip notices for the students in each grade. The museum trip was for 3 grades. How many notices did he print? _____

19. It costs $5 for each student to enter the museum. How much money did Mr. Sims need for 909 students to enter the museum?

_____

20. 600 students from another school joined the 909 students who were with Mr. Sims. The museum provided a study guide for each student. The study guides cost the museum $2 each to print. How much did it cost the museum to provide study guides for all of the students? _____

Name _____ Date _____

Problem-Solving Practice

4NS3.3, 4NS3.2

Multiply by Tens

Solve.

1. Teams of 16 students are helping the town clean the park. There are 20 teams in all. How many students are cleaning the park?

   _____

2. Students are going on a field trip in 10 buses. Each bus carries 35 students. How many students can go on the field trip?

   _____

3. Mr. Parker arranged 1 van for every 12 students to travel to the zoo. A total of 40 vans were needed. How many students went on the trip?

   _____

4. It cost $14 to buy tickets for each students to go to the petting zoo. Mr. Parker bought tickets for 30 students. How much did the tickets cost?

   _____

5. The 32 caretakers make sure that all of the animals are checked on each day at the zoo. How many animals are at the zoo if each caretaker checks on 30 animals?

   _____

6. 27 students run in a charity race to raise money for the zoo. Thirteen of the students each raise $20. The rest of the students each raise $30. How much did the students raise in all?

   _____

Name _____ Date _____

Homework Practice

Estimate Products

Estimate each product.

1. 37 × 22 _____   **2.** 878 × 41 _____

3. 49 × 16 _____   **4.** 250 × 12 _____

5. 68 × 22 _____   **6.** 688 × 19 _____

7. 36 × 81 _____   **8.** 563 × 29 _____

9. 714 × 11 _____   **10.** 141 × 78 _____

Estimate to solve.

11. The price of a bus ticket is $39. About how much will tickets cost for a group of 58 passengers?

_____

12. An airline ticket costs $285. About how much will tickets cost for a group of 37 people?

_____

Spiral Review

Multiply. (Lesson 8–1)

13. 35 × 10 _____   **14.** $723 × 20 _____

15. $58 × 40 _____   **16.** 448 × 40 _____

17. $89 × 30 _____   **18.** 58 × 60 _____

19. 54 × 80 _____   **20.** 98 × 80 _____

21. 43 × 40 _____   **22.** $51 × 50 _____

23. 45 × 80 _____   **24.** $663 × 30 _____

25. 99 × 90 _____   **26.** 39 × 70 _____

27. 75 × 50 _____   **28.** 87 × 20 _____

29. 658 × 50 _____   **30.** 52 × 60 _____

Name _____ Date _____

Problem-Solving Practice

Estimate Products

Solve.

1. Each of 32 classrooms has 4 computers. About how many computers are there in all?

   _____

2. A new keyboard for the computer costs $49. The school is buying 18 keyboards. About how much will they cost?

   _____

3. There are 42 times for students to work in the computer lab during one week. If 19 students can work in the computer lab at one time, about how many students can work in the computer lab during one week?

   _____

4. The school is buying 28 new computers for the computer lab. One computer costs $812. About how much will all of the computers cost?

   _____

5. The school district is buying laser printers for 62 schools. Each printer costs $898. About how much will all the printers cost?

   _____

6. The school district is buying software for virus protection. Each software package costs $48. There are 685 computers all together in the district's schools. About how much will the software cost?

   _____

Name _____ Date _____

Homework Practice

4MR1.0, 4NS3.0

Problem-Solving Strategy

Solve. Use the *act it out* strategy.

1. The Diving Club offers 4 beginning diving classes each day. Each class has room for 6 people. How many people can take classes in 30 days? _____

2. A fishing guide charges $25 per hour. He works 6 hours per day for 5 days. How much money does the guide earn? _____

3. During one week, 5 sailboats are rented for a total of 16 hours each. The rental cost is $25 per hour. Altogether, how much is paid for these rentals? _____

4. The aquarium charges $12 admission and $6 for a tour. A group of 20 people goes to the aquarium and takes the tour. How much money does the group spend? _____

5. Amanda rents a canoe and a life preserver from 2:00 P.M. to 5:00 P.M. A canoe costs $12 per hour. A life preserver costs $2 per hour. How much does Amanda spend? _____

6. Jenny rented a rowboat for 2 hours in the morning. After lunch, she rented another rowboat for 3 hours. For how many minutes did she rent the boat? _____

Spiral Review   **Estimate each product. (Lesson 8–2)**

7. 26×3 _____   8. 478×41 _____

9. 23×7 _____   10. 850×12 _____

11. 78×32 _____   12. 618×19 _____

13. 96×11 _____   14. 275×29 _____

15. 211×5 _____   16. 325×52 _____

17. Circle all of the numbers on this page that are multiples of tens.

Name _____ Date _____

Homework Practice

4NS3.2, 4NS3.3

Multiply Two-Digit Numbers

Multiply.

1.
$$\begin{array}{r} 26 \\ \times\ 35 \\ \hline \end{array}$$

2.
$$\begin{array}{r} \$46 \\ \times\ 35 \\ \hline \end{array}$$

3.
$$\begin{array}{r} 79 \\ \times\ 73 \\ \hline \end{array}$$

4.
$$\begin{array}{r} 73 \\ \times\ 51 \\ \hline \end{array}$$

5.
$$\begin{array}{r} 59 \\ \times\ 47 \\ \hline \end{array}$$

6.
$$\begin{array}{r} 94 \\ \times\ 61 \\ \hline \end{array}$$

7.
$$\begin{array}{r} 44 \\ \times\ 87 \\ \hline \end{array}$$

8.
$$\begin{array}{r} 77 \\ \times\ 22 \\ \hline \end{array}$$

9.
$$\begin{array}{r} \$63 \\ \times\ 58 \\ \hline \end{array}$$

10. $18 \times 92 =$ _____

11. $74 \times 33 =$ _____

12. $77 \times 94 =$ _____

13. $28 \times 19 =$ _____

14. $48 \times 26 =$ _____

15. $88 \times 62 =$ _____

16. $86 \times 43 =$ _____

17. $31 \times \$18 =$ _____

18. $27 \times 34 =$ _____

Spiral Review

Solve. (Lesson 8–3)

19. George had 3 fewer basketball cards yesterday than he does today. Yesterday he had 9 basketball cards. How many basketball cards does George have today? _____

20. Judy, Lakesha, and Tina each like a different color, either red, green, or blue. Judy likes green. Tina does not like blue. What color does Lakesha like? _____

Name _____ Date _____

Problem-Solving Practice

Multiply Two-Digit Numbers

Solve.

1. There are 15 students in each school club. There are 20 clubs in all. How many students are in all of the clubs? Multiply. Tell which method you used.

_____

2. There are 15 students in the art club. By the end of the school year, each student had made 23 pictures. How many pictures did the students make in all? Multiply. Tell which method you used.

_____

3. The fourth-grade students at Tremont School receive a ribbon if they read 50 books during the school year. There are 69 ribbons given out at the end of the year. How many books did the students read in all? Multiply. Tell which method you used.

_____

4. There are 27 students in Mr. Jacob's class. By the end of the school year, each student will have completed 72 tasks on the class schedule. How many tasks will have been completed? Multiply. Tell which method you used.

_____

5. The town's camera store bought 98 cameras for school photography clubs to use. Each camera cost $57. How much did the cameras cost in all? Multiply. Tell which method you used.

_____

6. There are 35 students in the photography club at Columbus School. Each student was given enough rolls of film to take 72 photos. How many photos did the students take in all? Multiply. Tell which method you used.

_____

Name _____ Date _____

Homework Practice

Multiply Three-Digit Numbers by Two-Digit Numbers

Multiply.

1. 185 × 18 _____

2. 152 × 83 _____

3. 525 × 63 _____

4. 467 × 81 _____

5. 149 × 21 _____

6. 555 × 28 _____

7. 542 × 25 _____

8. 336 × 92 _____

9. 342 × 19 _____

10. 521 × 52 _____

11. 417 × 23 _____

12. 643 × 26 _____

13. 950 × 48 _____

14. 311 × 11 _____

15. 322 × 35 _____

16. 229 × 45 _____

17. 661 × 78 _____

18. 738 × 22 _____

19. 120 × 42 _____

20. 620 × 33 _____

Spiral Review

Multiply. (Lesson 8–4)

21. 25 × 62 _____

22. 19 × 38 _____

23. 95 × 82 _____

24. 22 × 17 _____

25. 85 × 21 _____

26. 49 × 11 _____

27. 62 × 45 _____

28. 79 × 63 _____

29. 38 × 26 _____

30. 45 × 18 _____

31. 75 × 85 _____

32. 66 × 27 _____

33. 92 × 37 _____

34. 42 × 79 _____

35. Look back at exercises 21–34 and circle all factors that are multiples of 5.

8–5

Problem-Solving Practice

4NS3.2, 4NS3.3

Multiply Three-Digit Numbers by Two-Digit Numbers

Solve.

1. Each art class uses 231 pipe cleaners for a project. How many pipe cleaners will 15 classes use? Multiply. Check that the answer is reasonable.

   _____

2. A box of art supplies costs $202. How much do 22 boxes cost? Multiply. Check that the answer is reasonable.

   _____

3. Each week, 989 cars drive through the wildlife park. How many cars drive through the park in 24 weeks? Multiply. Check that the answer is reasonable.

   _____

4. A classroom set of books about space exploration costs $234. There are 16 classes. How much will books for all of the classes cost? Multiply. Check that the answer is reasonable.

   _____

5. The tile crew can lay 878 tiles in one day. How many tiles can the crew lay in 62 days? Multiply. Check that the answer is reasonable.

   _____

6. There are 981 floor tiles in one classroom in the school. How many floor tiles will it take to replace the tiles in 28 classrooms? Multiply. Check that the answer is reasonable.

   _____

Name _____ Date _____

Homework Practice

Problem-Solving Investigation

Use any strategy to solve. Tell what strategy you used.

1. It costs $216 to buy 24 tickets to the water park. How much does each ticket cost? Tell which method you used. _____

_____

2. There are 156 beads. They are divided into 12 equal groups. How many beads are in each group? Tell which method you used.

_____

_____

3. For a long-distance race, $175 was collected from each of 9 runners. How much was collected in all? Tell which method you used.

_____

_____

4. For a bicycle race, there are 432 cyclists. Each cyclist paid $12 to enter the race. How much money did the cyclists pay in all? Tell which method you used.

_____

_____

5. The owner of the hobby store pays $92 for an order of 23 model car kits. How much does each model car kit cost? Tell which method you used. _____

_____

6. There were 200 model car kits delivered to the hobby store. They were packed in 25 boxes. How many model car kits were in each box? Tell which method you used. _____

_____

 **Spiral Review** **Multiply. (Lesson 8–5)**

7. $801 \times 86 =$ _____

8. $631 \times 12 =$ _____

9. $511 \times 59 =$ _____

10. $775 \times 24 =$ _____

11. $362 \times 42 =$ _____

12. $933 \times 96 =$ _____

13. $339 \times 33 =$ _____

14. $460 \times 71 =$ _____

15. $823 \times 69 =$ _____

Name _____ Date _____

Homework Practice

Multiply Greater Numbers

Multiply.

1. $1,560 \times 27 =$ _____

2. $5,883 \times 39 =$ _____

3. $3,442 \times 32 =$ _____

4. $16,846 \times 21 =$ _____

5. $6,251 \times 54 =$ _____

6. $\$31,067 \times 40 =$ _____

7. $3,166 \times 21 =$ _____

8. $\$40,724 \times 32 =$ _____

9. $4,351 \times 67 =$ _____

10. $\$25,331 \times 48 =$ _____

11. $2,909 \times 44 =$ _____

12. $\$37,550 \times 38 =$ _____

13. Antonio runs 2 miles a day. In one mile there is 5,280 feet. How many feet does he run in 2 weeks? _____

14. If a panda bear eats 84 pounds of fresh bamboo sprouts every day, how many pounds of bamboo do 12 pandas eat in two weeks?

_____

15. There are 2,734 miles between Seattle, Washington and Miami, Florida. If Consuelo travels round trip from Miami to Seattle 6 times, how many miles does she travel altogether?

_____

Spiral Review

Solve. (Lesson 8–6)

16. Brady is counting the money in his piggy bank. He has $0.56. He has 3 kinds of coins and 8 coins in all. What coins does he have?

_____

17. Sara is thinking of two numbers that have a sum of 15 and a product of 56. What are the two numbers?

_____

18. Marc has 15 trophies. Four of the trophies are for track. He has two times as many swimming trophies as track trophies. The rest of the trophies are for soccer. How many soccer trophies does he have?

_____

8-7

Problem-Solving Practice

Multiply Greater Numbers

4NS3.3, 4MR2.1

Solve.

1. Jamie travels 3,056 miles each year. How many miles does Jamie travel in 15 years?

   _____

2. Fourteen members of the crafts club are making necklaces. It takes 202 beads to make each necklace. How many beads will they need if they each make 5 necklaces?

   _____

3. An elephant weighs 13,500 pounds. How much would 25 elephants the same size weigh all together?

   _____

4. Jason is taking a bus to visit his grandparents. The bus trip is 113 miles each way. How many miles will Jason travel to and from his grandparents' house? Write the multiplication sentence and solve.

   _____

5. Jack is a pilot for a large airline. He plans on retiring in 11 years. Every week, he follows the same schedule of flights. He knows that he flies 78,434 miles each year. How many miles will he fly

   before he retires? _____

6. The city parks commission wants to build a new park. The model has 6 tennis courts. Each tennis court will cost $92,378. The city does not want to pay more than $550,000 for all 6 courts. How

   much will the tennis courts cost? _____

   Will the city be able to build all of them? _____

Name _____ Date _____

Homework Practice

4NS3.4

Division with Remainders

Divide. Check each answer.

1. $6\overline{)56}$ _____

2. $5\overline{)42}$ _____

3. $6\overline{)25}$ _____

4. $2\overline{)32}$ _____

5. $5\overline{)41}$ _____

6. $9\overline{)53}$ _____

7. $6\overline{)54}$ _____

8. $6\overline{)34}$ _____

9. $8\overline{)21}$ _____

10. $7\overline{)35}$ _____

11. $72 \div 8$ _____

12. $15 \div 7$ _____

13. $64 \div 7$ _____

14. $49 \div 3$ _____

15. $28 \div 3$ _____

16. Andy's mom would not tell her age, but she did give these clues:

    Divide my age by 4, and it is 10. I am between 50 and 30. _____

Spiral Review (Lesson 8-7)

Multiply.

17. $2,363 \times 99$ _____

18. $4,144 \times 33$ _____

19. $26,706 \times 67$ _____

20. $34,371 \times 42$ _____

21. Through his telescope, Jose identified 12 stars each night for

    64 nights. How many different stars has Jose seen? _____

22. Look back over this page. Circle all of the numbers on the page that
    can be divided by 2 without a remainder.

Name _____ Date _____

Problem-Solving Practice

Division with Remainders

Divide. Check each answer.

1. The zoo gives the nature club 47 wildlife posters. There are 8 members in the club. They want to divide the posters evenly among the members. How many posters will each member get? How many posters are left?

_____

2. The science club has 43 members. Ms. Reed wants to divide them into groups of 6. How many groups of 6 will there be? How many groups will have an extra member?

_____

3. Nine members of the ecology club are writing reports about trees. They have chosen 53 kinds of trees. Each member writes a report about the same number of trees. How many reports will each one write? How many members will have to write an extra report?

_____

4. Seven members of the ecology club are also making leaf books. They will gather information about 44 kinds of leaves. How many leaves will each of the 7 members study? How many members will study an extra kind of leaf?

_____

5. There are 63 endangered mammals in the U.S. Five students plan to research each mammal. If each student takes an equal number of mammals to research, how many mammals will they study? How many students will have an extra mammal to research?

_____

6. Nine students want to learn more about endangered birds in the U.S. There are 76 endangered birds. If each of the students takes an equal number of endangered birds, how many birds will each student study? How many students will have an extra bird to study?

_____

Name _____ Date _____

Homework Practice

Divide Multiples of 10, 100, and 1,000

Divide. Use patterns.

1. $6\overline{)300}$ _____

2. $5\overline{)2,000}$ _____

3. $4\overline{)3,600}$ _____

4. $2\overline{)1,000}$ _____

5. $6\overline{)1,200}$ _____

6. $5\overline{)1,000}$ _____

7. $2\overline{)1,800}$ _____

8. $8\overline{)4,000}$ _____

9. $9\overline{)2,700}$ _____

10. $8\overline{)3,200}$ _____

11. $4\overline{)4,000}$ _____

12. $3\overline{)2,100}$ _____

13. $5\overline{)3,500}$ _____

14. $6\overline{)2,400}$ _____

15. $7\overline{)2,800}$ _____

Complete the table.

16. Divide by 5

Input	Output
1,500	_____
3,000	_____
6,000	_____

Spiral Review

Divide. Check each answer. (Lesson 9-1)

17. $61 \div 3$ _____

18. $21 \div 5$ _____

19. $80 \div 7$ _____

20. $12 \div 5$ _____

21. $14 \div 6$ _____

22. $51 \div 7$ _____

23. $28 \div 6$ _____

24. $72 \div 3$ _____

25. Mrs. Jones has 36 calculators. She has to divide them between 3 groups of students. How many calculators will each group get?

_____

9-2

Problem-Solving Practice

4NS3.0

Divide Multiples of 10, 100, and 1,000

Divide. Use patterns.

1. There are 8 people taking a trip to New York City. The total price of the trip is $8,000. How much will the trip cost each person?

   _____

2. The bus will travel 4,500 miles. Five people will take turns driving. If each person drives the same amount, how many miles will each

   person drive? _____

3. When the trip is over, they will have spent a total of 80 hours driving in the bus, over a total of 10 days. How many hours will

   they average driving each day? _____

4. The plan is for 8 people to be gone 20 days. 10 days will be spent sight seeing in New York City. They set aside $3,200 for spending money in New York City. How much does each person have to spend each day?

   _____

5. For the 10 driving days, the 8 people will spend a total of $1,600 on hotel rooms. How much will each person spend each night on hotel rooms?

   _____

6. For the 10 days in NYC, the 8 people will spend a total of $2,400 on hotel rooms. How much does each room cost per night if 4 people stay in each room?

   _____

Name _____ Date _____

Homework Practice

4MR1.1, 4NS3.0

Problem-Solving Strategy

Solve. Use the *guess and check* strategy.

1. Jim's baseball team has played 5 games so far this season. Jim hit 5 home runs. Justin hit twice as many home runs as Jim hit. They are the only boys who have hit home runs this season. How many

   home runs have been hit? _____

2. Joe's parents have used 29 gallons of gasoline this month. Last month, June, they used twice that amount. The month before, May, they used twice what they did in June. How many gallons of

   gasoline did they use in May? _____

3. 510 is the total number of tickets that can be sold for the baseball game. If the school bought 25 tickets and a neighborhood club bought twice as many tickets as the school, how many tickets can

   still be sold? _____

4. Linda bought three items from the list below.

peanuts $1, a ring $5, a coloring book $3, a stuffed animal $6

   She gave the cashier $10 and got no change. Which three items did she buy?

   _____

   _____

Spiral Review

Divide. Use patterns. (Lesson 9-2)

5. $2\overline{)200}$ _____

6. $8\overline{)400}$ _____

7. $3\overline{)1,500}$ _____

8. $2,400 \div 6$ _____

9. $3,600 \div 6$ _____

10. $5,600 \div 7$ _____

Name _____ Date _____

Homework Practice

Estimate Quotients

4NS3.4

Estimate. Check your estimate.

1. $8\overline{)242}$ _____
2. $8\overline{)641}$ _____
3. $5\overline{)402}$ _____
4. $6\overline{)241}$ _____
5. $7\overline{)563}$ _____
6. $4\overline{)121}$ _____
7. $3\overline{)273}$ _____
8. $5\overline{)149}$ _____
9. $8\overline{)161}$ _____
10. $7\overline{)494}$ _____
11. $9\overline{)184}$ _____
12. $9\overline{)629}$ _____
13. $3\overline{)301}$ _____
14. $9\overline{)453}$ _____
15. $6\overline{)331}$ _____
16. $2\overline{)804}$ _____
17. $6\overline{)422}$ _____
18. $5\overline{)247}$ _____
19. $9\overline{)625}$ _____
20. $8\overline{)639}$ _____

Spiral Review

Solve. Use the *guess and check* strategy. (Lesson 9–3)

21. Phil had 3 baseball cards. One of them cost twice as much as the other two. If the total amount that he paid for the cards was $40, how much did each card cost? _____

22. Jan's mother said that Jan could have 2 tickets to a movie, 5 tickets for fruit smoothies, or 7 tickets for rides at an amusement park. Jan had to choose what she wanted. Each ticket was worth $5. Jan's mother spent a total of $10. What did Jan choose?

_____

23. Look back over this page and circle all the numbers that can be rounded to 300. Then draw a box around any numbers that can be rounded to 600.

Name _____ Date _____

Problem-Solving Practice

Estimate Quotients

Estimate. Check your estimate.

1. 2,670 people attended rock concerts in a huge arena. There were 5 different bands playing with about the same number of people watching each band. About how many people attended each concert?

_____

2. Jill earned 1,690 points in math class. Half of the points were for 8 tests. Jill scored about the same on each test. About how many points did she score on each test?

_____

3. One project is worth 550 points. There are 8 parts to the project. If each part is worth the same number of points, about how many points is each part worth?

_____

4. Mr. Kirk graded 4,212 word problems. Each problem took about the same amount of time to grade. Mr. Kirk graded about 4 word problems per minute. About how many minutes did he spent grading?

_____

5. A test is worth 639 points. If each question is worth 8 points, about how many questions are on the test?

_____

6. Mary is practicing for a math competition. She should be able to calculate about 9 problems within 180 minutes. About how long will she have for each problem?

_____

Name _____ Date _____

Homework Practice

4NS3.4, 4MR2.1

Two-Digit Quotients

Divide.

1. $21 \div 4$ _____

2. $89 \div 6$ _____

3. $170 \div 3$ _____

4. $442 \div 5$ _____

5. $712 \div 8$ _____

6. $145 \div 3$ _____

7. $165 \div 9$ _____

8. $368 \div 7$ _____

9. $125 \div 7$ _____

10. $219 \div 4$ _____

11. $324 \div 9$ _____

12. $364 \div 7$ _____

13. $498 \div 5$ _____

14. $642 \div 7$ _____

15. $432 \div 8$ _____

16. $681 \div 7$ _____

17. $251 \div 8$ _____

18. $219 \div 7$ _____

19. $868 \div 9$ _____

20. $765 \div 8$ _____

Spiral Review   Estimate. Check your estimate.

(Lesson 9-4)

21. $254 \div 5$ _____

22. $349 \div 7$ _____

23. $639 \div 8$ _____

24. $487 \div 7$ _____

25. Look back over the page. Circle all dividends that can be divided in half with no remainder.

9–5

Problem-Solving Practice

Two-Digit Quotients

4NS3.4, 4MR2.1

Divide.

1. Pat earned $65. He worked 5 days. How much did he earn each

   day? _____

2. Pat's job was to feed and walk his neighbors' dog while they were
   on vacation. During the 5 days that he worked, he spent a total of
   150 minutes with the dog. How many minutes each day did he

   work? _____

3. Matt earned $60. He worked 4 days. How much did he earn each

   day? _____

4. Matt's job was to rake leaves. Each day it took him a total of
   180 minutes to rake 2 yards. How long did he spend raking each

   yard? _____

5. Sam earned $70 helping his father paint the garage. He was paid
   per hour. If he spent 7 hours total helping his father, how much

   was he paid for each hour he worked? _____

6. Jason worked a total of 77 hours mowing lawns, pulling weeds,
   and raking leaves for the 7 houses on his street. How long did it
   take him to mow the lawn, pull the weeds, and rake each yard?

   _____

Name _____ Date _____

Homework Practice

Problem-Solving Investigation

Use any strategy to solve.

1. Ellie has 8 coins that equal 92 cents. What are the coins?

   _____

2. Meg is going to a birthday party at 6 p.m. She gets home from school at 3 p.m. It will take her 1 hour to do her homework, 30 minutes to get dressed, and 30 minutes to get to the party. How much extra time does she have?

   _____

3. Sandy is creating a flower basket with 12 white, yellow, and orange flowers in it. The order she wants the flowers in is white, orange, yellow. If she always has a white beside an orange and a yellow beside an orange, how many orange flowers will she need to have?

   _____

4. What is the next number in the pattern 20,000; 4,000; 800; 160; _____
   What is the pattern?

   _____

Spiral Review

Divide. (Lesson 9–5)

5. 2)‾57‾ _____

6. 4)‾79‾ _____

7. 5)‾86‾ _____

8. 2)‾93‾ _____

9. 3)‾46‾ _____

10. 8)‾99‾ _____

Name _____ Date _____

Homework Practice

Three-Digit Quotients

Divide.

1. $5\overline{)569}$

2. $3\overline{)673}$

3. $5\overline{)675}$

4. $5\overline{)997}$

5. $3\overline{)334}$

6. $7\overline{)987}$

7. $8\overline{)895}$

8. $6\overline{)674}$

9. $9\overline{)999}$

10. $3\overline{)534}$

Spiral Review Use any strategy to solve. (Lesson 9–6)

11. What is the next number in the pattern 16, 32, 64, 128, ___ ?
What is the pattern?

_____

12. Janice has 8 coins that total 80 cents. What are the coins?

_____

Name _____ Date _____

Problem-Solving Practice

Three-Digit Quotients

Divide.

1. Ann needs to read 417 pages in 3 days. How many pages should she read each day?

   _____

2. Jamal has read 564 pages in 5 hours. How many pages of the book did he read per hour?

   _____

3. Kendra was awarded $250 for her hard work. She put half in the bank. How much did she put in the bank?

   _____

4. Eric and his company collected 840 children's books to give to a community center. The books were then divided equally between 7 families. How many books did each family receive?

   _____

5. Before Ann and John graduated from high school, they had read 1,520 stories to children. They read the same number of stories each time that they read to children. For 8 years they read to children. How many stories did they read each year?

   _____

Name _____ Date _____

Homework Practice

Quotients with Zeros

Divide.

1. 5)512

2. 5)543

3. 4)837

4. 3)629

5. 3)926

6. 6)658

7. 2)612

8. 4)822

9. 4)436

10. 2)611

Divide. (Lesson 9-7)

11. 7)878

12. 6)684

Solve.

13. 4 plums fit in a box. How many boxes can be filled with 968 plums?

_____

9–8

Problem-Solving Practice

Quotients with Zeros

4NS3.4, 4NS3.2

Divide.

1. The camping club spent $202 on 2 tents. How much did each tent cost?

   _____

2. The animal park sold 315 tickets in 3 days. If the same number of tickets were sold each day, how many tickets were sold?

   _____

3. Ms. Jones took 9 children to the water park. The children's tickets cost $180. How much did each ticket cost?

   _____

4. The water park had 1,320 visitors on Friday, Saturday, and Sunday. There were an equal number of visitors each day. How many visitors were there each day?

   _____

5. There are 2 large gym classes with 3 teams in each class. Each team needs an equal number of balls to play a game. There are 300 balls in all. How many balls will each team use?

   _____

Name _____ Date _____

Homework Practice

Divide Greater Numbers

Divide.

1. $5\overline{)5{,}098}$

10. $2\overline{)8{,}642}$

2. $6\overline{)6{,}485}$

11. $3\overline{)\$4{,}743}$

3. $2\overline{)\$3{,}458}$

12. $5\overline{)\$8{,}115}$

4. $6\overline{)7{,}349}$

13. $3\overline{)83{,}765}$

5. $7\overline{)8{,}655}$

14. $2\overline{)60{,}567}$

6. $5\overline{)5{,}437}$

15. $4\overline{)84{,}219}$

7. $9\overline{)\$9{,}950}$

16. $3\overline{)98{,}651}$

8. $8\overline{)8{,}349}$

17. $4\overline{)73{,}633}$

9. $3\overline{)6{,}980}$

18. $4\overline{)63{,}683}$

Spiral Review   Divide. (Lesson 9-8)

19. $4\overline{)427}$

22. $3\overline{)929}$

20. $6\overline{)641}$

23. $7\overline{)745}$

21. $2\overline{)815}$

24. $3\overline{)629}$

25. Look back over the page. Circle all the numbers that can be rounded to a number greater than 90,000.

Name _____ Date _____

Problem-Solving Practice

Divide Greater Numbers

Divide.

1. The hobby store had 3,126 beads. They put them into bags of 6 beads each. How many bags did they have?

   _____bags

2. The hobby store had 4,212 beads. They put an equal number of beads into 8 boxes. How many beads were in each box?

   _____ beads

   How many beads were left over?

   _____ beads left over

3. The community center is putting new floor tiles in 6 rooms. They have 2,250 floor tiles for all of the rooms. Each room is the same size. How many floor tiles will be used in each room?

   _____ tiles

4. Best Floor Company has 8 orders for the same number of floor tiles. They have 18,965 tiles in stock to fill the orders. How many floor tiles are in each order?

   _____ tiles

   How many floor tiles will they have left?

   _____ tiles left

5. The owner of the garden store ordered 12,635 packets of flower seeds. He stored the seeds by putting an equal number of packets into each of 6 bins. How many packets went into each bin?

   _____

6. The garden store owner paid $62,472 for flower bulbs. She made 4 equal payments for the flower bulbs. How much did she pay each time?

   $ _____

Name _____ Date _____

Homework Practice

Solid Figures

Identify each figure. Then tell the number of faces, edges and vertices.

1.

_____

_____

_____

2.

_____

_____

_____

Identify the solid figure each net makes.

3.

_____

4.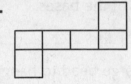

_____

5. This solid figure has 0 faces, 0 edges, and 0 vertices. What is it?

_____

Spiral Review   Divide. Use estimation to check.

6.  7)3,720

_____

7. 50,250 ÷ 5 =

_____

8. Raul pays $1,008 total for lunch over 8 months. If he pays the same amount each month, how much does he pay each month?

_____

Name _____ Date _____

Problem-Solving Practice

Solid Figures

Solve.

1. Molly has a set of wooden blocks. This is one of her blocks. Tell how many faces, edges, and vertices the block has.

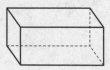

_____

2. Molly's set of wooden blocks also has a block that is in the shape of a cylinder. How many bases does the cylinder block have? Describe the shape of the bases.

_____

3. Natasha bought a large bead to hang from a necklace. The bead has 5 faces, 9 edges, and 6 vertices. What kind of figure was the bead?

_____

4. Mel has a board game that uses 10 pieces shaped like the one below. How many bases does each game piece have? Describe the shape of the bases.

_____

5. Iman and his father are making an end table for their living room. When they are done, the end table has 6 faces, 12 edges, and 8 vertices. What kind of figure did Iman and his father make?

_____

_____

Name _____ Date _____

Homework Practice

Plane Figures

Identify each polygon.

1. _____

2. _____

3. 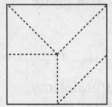 _____

4. 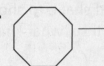 _____

Identify the shapes in the figure.

5. _____

Tell whether the shape is a polygon.

6. _____

7. _____

Spiral Review   Identify each figure. Then tell how many faces, edges and vertices it has. (Lesson 10–1)

8. _____

9. _____

_____

_____

Identify the solid figure each net would make.

13. 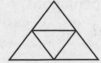 _____

Name _____ Date _____

Problem-Solving Practice

4MG3.0

Plane figures

1. Nick and his brother are building a tree house. It will have 2 windows. One window is shaped like a square, and the other is shaped like a rectangle. What do these two shapes have in common?

_____

2. Nick's brother draws a 3-sided shape to show what the roof of the tree house will look like. Is it a polygon? If so, what kind of polygon?

_____

3. Sara is playing a chalk game on the sidewalk. She draws a large quadrilateral first. Inside the quadrilateral, she draws the same figure 10 times. The figure is not a polygon. What figure did she draw?

_____

4. Sara uses her chalk to draw a line diagonally through her quadrilateral. Now, instead of one quadrilateral, she has two of the same polygons. What shapes did she make?

_____

5. For a homework assignment, Dina must find polygons around her town and draw them. She goes down to the harbor, where she sees a boat like the one below. She draws it, but the teacher says it is not a polygon. Why?

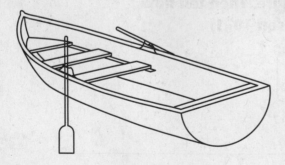

_____

_____

6. Sean used toothpicks to make the following shapes: 2 triangles, 3 pentagons, 4 quadrilaterals, and 6 hexagons. How many toothpicks did he use?

_____

140

Name _____ Date _____

Homework Practice

4MG3.0, 4MR1.1

Problem-Solving Strategy: Look for a Pattern

1. ALGEBRA: Copy and complete the table. What is the pattern?

Input	Output
4	16
9	36
2	8
	24
3	

Pattern? _____

2. Describe the pattern below. Then find the missing number.

1, 3, 9 , _____ , 81

Spiral Review

Identify each shape.

3.

_____

4.

_____

5.

_____

6.

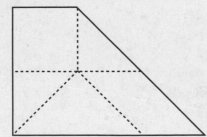

_____

Identify the shapes in the figure.

7.

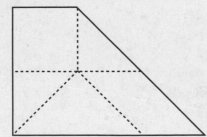

_____

Tell whether the shape is a polygon.

8.

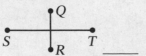

_____

9.

_____

10.

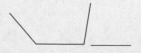

_____

10-4

Homework Practice

Lines, Line Segments, and Rays

4MG3.1

Identify each figure.

1. X •————————• Y _____

2. V •————————•→ W _____

3. ↖ T
   3. •
          • U
              ↘ _____

Describe the figure.

4. 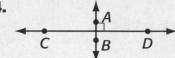 _____

5.  _____

6.
   K
   I •——•——•——• J
   ↙ L _____

Draw an example of each.

7. ray *CD*

8. line segment *FG*

Spiral Review

Solve.

9. Melissa is planting flowers in a pattern. If she continues to plant a red, then pink, then yellow flower, what color will be the eighth

flower? _____

10. Describe the pattern below. Then find the missing number.

1, 4, 16, _____, 256

10-4

Problem-Solving Practice

(4MG3.1)

Lines, Line Segments, and Rays

Solve.

1. During Hillary's softball game, she ran from first base and stopped at second base. Did her path form a line, line segment, parallel lines, or intersecting lines?

   _____

2. Jenna looks at the letter T. Does the letter T form a line segment, parallel line segments, or perpendicular line segments?

   _____

3. Ryan's ski instructor tells him that he should keep his skis parallel. Draw how Ryan's skis should look.

4. Ryan accidentally crosses the tips of his skis and falls down. What word describes the type of line that Ryan's crossed skis created?

   _____

5. Louis gets lost on the way to Josh's house. He calls and says he is on Main Street. To get to Josh's house from Main Street, Louis must turn left on First Avenue. Is First Avenue parallel to Main Street?

   _____

6. Josh lives at the corner of First Avenue and Maple Street. How might he describe the way the streets meet at his house?

   _____

   _____

10–5

Homework Practice

Angles

4MG3.5

Write the measure of the angle in degrees and as a fraction of a full turn.

1.

_____

2.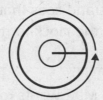

_____

Classify each angle as *right*, *acute*, or *obtuse*.

3.

_____

4.

_____

5.

_____

Spiral Review

Describe the figures. (Lesson 10–4)

6.
M
N

_____

7.
P
O

_____

8.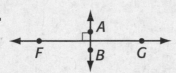

A
F   B   G

_____

9.

T   U

V   W

_____

Solve.

1. Matt looks at the clock and sees that it is 12:55. What type of angle do the hands of the clock form?

   _____

2. Now the hour is 1:00. Matt wants to wait until the hands of the clock form a right angle. Until what hour must he wait?

   _____

3. The clock in Ms. Alston's classroom reads 2:15. She tells the students that class will be over when the hands on the clock next form an obtuse angle, and the minute hand is pointing directly to a number on the clockface. What time will class be over?

   _____

4. Jake goes to a friend's house at 2:30. He stays until the hands on the clock form an acute angle. What is the earliest time he could have left?

   _____

5. Elise set her alarm clock for 50 minutes after 2 on the morning she was leaving for her camping trip. She fell back asleep for 10 minutes. She finally left the house at 3:25. What type of angle did the hands on the clock form when her alarm went off?

   _____

   What type of angle did the hands on the clock form when she

   woke up the second time? _____

   What type of angle did the hands on the clock form when she left

   the house? _____

6. Elise left her house at 3:25. She arrived at the trail head at 6:00. In the time it took Elise to arrive at the campsite, how many times did the hands on a clock form right angles?

   _____

Name _____ Date _____

Homework Practice

Problem-Solving Investigation

Use any method shown below to solve. Tell what method you used.

- Work backward
- Reasonable answers
- Act it out
- Guess and check
- Look for a pattern

1. Justin can run 2 blocks in 1 minute. If he is 8 blocks from home, is it reasonable to say he can run home in 5 minutes?

_____

Strategy:_____

2. Sarah watched the band march by in a pattern. She saw a trumpet, flute, saxophone, drum, trumpet, flute, saxophone, drum pattern. What are the next three instruments she will see?

_____

Strategy:_____

Spiral Review
Write the measure of the angle in degrees and as a fraction of a full turn. (Lesson 10–5)

3.

_____

4.

_____

Classify each angle as *right*, *acute*, or *obtuse*.

5.

_____

6.

_____

Name _____ Date _____

Homework Practice

Triangles

Classify each triangle. Use *isosceles, equilateral,* or *scalene* and *acute, right,* or *obtuse*.

1.
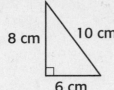

_____

2.
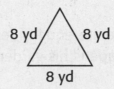

_____

3.
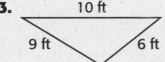

_____

4.
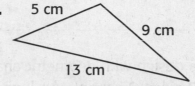

_____

Spiral Review

Use any strategy shown below to solve. (Lesson 10-6)

Tell what strategy you used.

- Work backward
- Reasonable answers
- Act it out
- Guess and check
- Look for a pattern

5. A number is multiplied by 3. Then 8 is subtracted from the

product. The result is 4. What was the original number? _____

Strategy: _____

6. Rebecca wants to bake banana bread, do her homework, call
her friend, and clean her room before soccer practice. It takes
65 minutes to make banana bread, 35 minutes to do her
homework, 20 minutes to call her friend, and 15 minutes to clean
her room. Her soccer practice starts in 2 hours. Does she have

enough time to do everything she wants to do? _____

Strategy: _____

Name _____ Date _____

Problem-Solving Practice

4MG3.7

Triangles

Solve.

1. Jon's garden has 3 sides. None are equal sides and there are no equal angles. What type of shape is his garden?

   _____

2. Santi has 3 sticks; two of them are 3 centimeters and one is 6 centimeters. Will he be able to make a triangle with them?

   _____

3. Brianne is making a design with geometric shapes. She draws a triangle that has 2 sides, 2 centimeters long. The triangle has 2 angles that are 70°. On a separate sheet of paper, draw a triangle like the one Brianne has drawn. What kind of triangle is it—isosceles, equilateral, or scalene?

   _____

   _____

4. If you draw an equilateral triangle and two sides are 3 inches what is the length of the third?

   _____

5. Bruno is making a drawing of the Pentagon. How many triangles will he need to draw to make this polygon, and how many sides will it have?

   _____

6. Alison is cutting out fabric. One side of the material is 10 feet, another side is 6 feet, and the third side is 8 feet. What shape is she cutting?

   _____

Name _____ Date _____

Homework Practice

Quadrilaterals

Classify each quadrilateral in as many ways as possible.

1.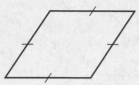

_____

2.

_____

3.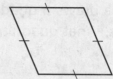

_____

4.

_____

5.

_____

6.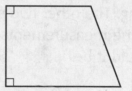

_____

Spiral Review

Classify each triangle. Use *isosceles*, *equilateral*, or *scalene* and *acute*, *right*, or *obtuse*. (Lesson 10–7)

7.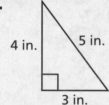
4 in. 5 in. 3 in.

_____

8.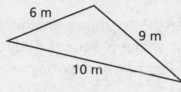
6 m 9 m 10 m

_____

9.
5 ft 8 ft 6 ft

_____

10.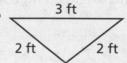
3 ft 2 ft 2 ft

_____

11.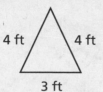
4 ft 4 ft 3 ft

_____

12.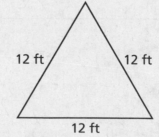
12 ft 12 ft 12 ft

_____

Name _____ Date _____

Problem-Solving Practice

Quadrilaterals

Solve.

1. Bonnie draws a quadrilateral with 4 equal sides, and 4 right angles. What quadrilateral is it?

_____

2. Santi's wallet is in the shape of a rectangle. Two sides are 2 inches long. The other two sides are 3 inches long. Chaz's wallet has the same measurements but is not a rectangle. What other shape could it be?

_____

3. Marcus draws a quadrilateral that has 4 equal sides, but no right angles. What quadrilateral might it be?

_____

4. Andy draws a square. Peter draws another shape that has 4 equal sides. Peter says his shape is square. Andy says it is not. What other shape might Peter have drawn?

_____

5. Kelly draws a shape with 4 sides of equal length. The shape has 2 obtuse angles and 2 acute angles. What shape does Kelly draw?

_____

6. Alison is cutting out fabric. The top of the material measures 1 ft, and the bottom measures 3 ft. Each side measures 2 ft. What shape is she cutting?

_____

Name _____ Date _____

Homework Practice

4MG3.2

Parts of a Circle

Identify the part of the circle shown.

1.

_____

3.

_____

5.

_____

2.

_____

4.

_____

6.

_____

Name the parts of the circle.

7. $\overline{GH}$

_____

8. $\overline{OK}$

_____

9. O

_____

10. $\overline{GO}$

_____

Spiral Review

possible. (Lesson 10-8)

Classify each quadrilateral in as many ways as

11.

_____

12.

_____

13.

_____

14.

_____

15.

_____

16.

_____

Name _____ Date _____

Problem-Solving Practice

Parts of a Circle

4MG3.2

Solve.

1. Beth looks at the clock when the school bell rings at 3:30. What part of a circle is the minute hand on the clock?

   _____

2. Beth notices that the clock has a straight crack on the left side. It reaches from the top to the bottom and through the center. What part of a circle is the crack?

   _____

3. Coach Spano wears a sports watch for soccer practice. She checks the time and sees that it is 6:00, time for practice to end. What is the part of a circle that is formed by the hands of the watch?

   _____

4. At soccer practice, the teammates stood in a circle and took turns kicking the ball to the person in the center. If the ball traveled in a straight line, what part of a circle did it make?

   _____

5. Joan made a pie that she cut into six pieces. She began by cutting the pie in half across the middle. What is the name of the line segment of her first cut?

   _____

6. After Joan cut the pie through the middle, she cut each half into 3 wedges. What part of a circle is one side of a wedge of the pie?

   _____

Name _____ Date _____

Homework Practice

4MG3.3

Geometry: Congruent

Tell whether the figures are congruent. Write *yes* or *no*.

1.
_____

2.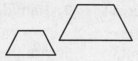
_____

3.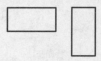
_____

4.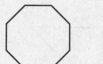
_____

5.
_____

6.
_____

Spiral Review   **Identify the part of the circle shown.**
(Lesson 10–9)

7.
_____

8.
_____

9.
_____

Name the parts of the circle.

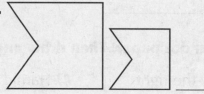

10. SW _____

11. WV _____

12. W _____

13. ST _____

Name _____ Date _____

Problem-Solving Practice

Geometry: Congruent

Tell whether the figures are congruent. Write *yes* or *no*.

1. Amy drew these two figures on dot paper. Look at the figures. Are they congruent?

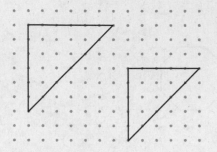

_____

2. Hamid looked at the ends of two wooden blocks. Are they congruent?

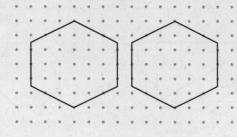

_____

Copy each figure on dot paper. Then draw one congruent figure.

3. Next, Amy drew the right triangle below. On a separate sheet of dot paper, copy the figure. Then, draw one congruent figure.

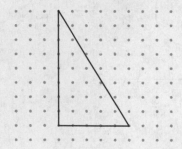

4. Hamid traced the end of another wooden block onto dot paper. The figure he traced looks like this. On a separate sheet of dot paper, copy the figure. Then, draw one congruent figure.

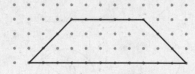

5. Inez wants to make two pentagons. On a separate sheet of dot paper, draw two congruent pentagons.

_____

Name _____ Date _____

Homework Practice

4MG3.4

Geometry: Symmetry

Tell whether each figure has line symmetry. Write *yes* or *no*. Then tell how many lines of symmetry the figure has.

1.  _____

3. 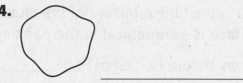 _____

2. _____

4.  _____

Tell whether the figure has rotational symmetry. Write *yes* or *no*.

5.  _____

7. 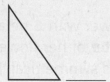 _____

6.  _____

8. 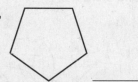 _____

Spiral Review   Tell whether the figures are congruent.
Write *yes* or *no*. (Lesson 11-1)

9. 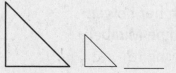 _____

10. 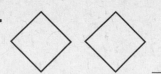 _____

11. 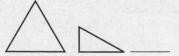 _____

12. _____

13. 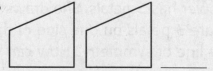 _____

14. 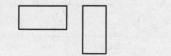 _____

Name _____ Date _____

Problem-Solving Practice

Geometry: Symmetry

Solve.

1. The pattern on Beth's floor is in the shape of a plus sign. She copies the shape onto paper and draws a dotted line through the center. Is the dotted line a line of symmetry?

   _____

2. Sam is painting a picture of his mother. If he wants to make sure her face is symmetrical in the painting, what can he do to the

   canvas before he begins? _____

   _____

   _____

3. Sheila draws this flower with 6 petals. Then she draws a dotted line through the center of her flower as shown here to find out whether the flower is symmetrical. Is the dotted line a line of symmetry on Sheila's flower?

   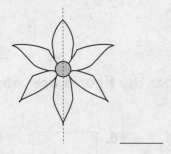

   _____

4. How many lines of symmetry can you draw through a square? _____

5. Mirabel is drawing a picture of a flower she found near their campsite. The flower has 5 petals. She draws a dotted line through her flower. There are 3 petals on one side of the line. Is the dotted line Mirabel drew a line of symmetry? How can you tell without drawing it?

   _____

   _____

   _____

   _____

Name _____ Date _____

Homework Practice

4MG1.4, 4AF1.4

Measurement: Perimeter

Find the perimeter of each figure.

1.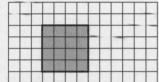

2.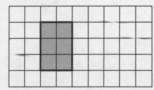

3.

_____   _____   _____

Find the perimeter of each figure in units.

4.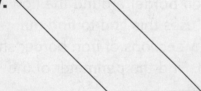

5.

6.

_____   _____   _____

Spiral Review   **Tell whether each figure has line symmetry. Write *yes* or *no*. If yes, tell how many lines of symmetry the figure has.**

7.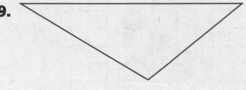

8.

_____   _____

Tell whether the figure has rotational symmetry. Write *yes* or *no*.

9.

10.

_____   _____

Problem-Solving Practice

4MG1.4, 4AF1.4

Measurement: Perimeter

Find the perimeter of each figure.

1. Jorge is drawing a design for a box car. He draws this rectangle to use as the base of the car. Find the perimeter of the rectangle.

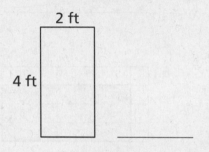

2 ft

4 ft

_____

2. The Hitoshi family plans to make a short sidewalk and patio in their backyard. First, they will need to place a frame around the space. This drawing shows the shape and dimensions of the frame they need to place. What is the frame's perimeter?

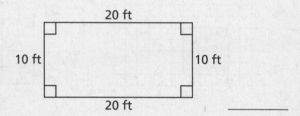

20 ft

10 ft   10 ft

20 ft

_____

3. Jorge uses this rectangle as a pattern for a picture of a building. What is the perimeter of his rectangle?

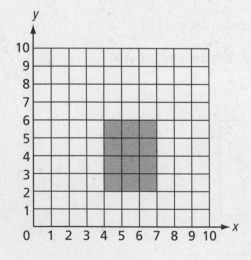

4. Mrs. Hitoshi decides to plant a flower bed next to the patio. She wants to use an iron border around the flower bed. She uses this grid to find out how many sections of iron border she will need. Find the perimeter of the flower bed.

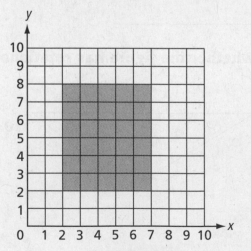

_____   _____

11-4

Homework Practice

4MR1.2, 4NS3.0

Problem-Solving Strategy: Solve a Simpler Problem

Solve. Use the *solve a simpler problem* strategy.

1. Nicholas had to make 6 cakes for the party. Each cake takes 12 minutes to mix, 21 minutes to bake, and 27 minutes to cool and decorate. How many hours will it take to make all 6 cakes? _____

2. Ricardo grows tomatoes in his garden. Each tomato plant yields 22 tomatoes each week. He has 5 tomato plants. How many tomatoes does he have after 4 weeks? _____

Spiral Review — **Find the perimeter of each figure. (Lesson 11–3)**

3.
```
        7 ft
    ┌─────────────┐
3 ft│             │
    └─────────────┘
```

_____

4.
```
    ┌──────────┐
15 yd│          │
    └──────────┘
      15 yd
```

_____

5.
```
  ┌──────┐
  │      │9 ft
  └──────┘
   9 ft
```

_____

6. 1 m ┌────────┐
        5 m

_____

Find the perimeter of each figure in units.

7.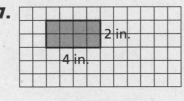

2 in.

4 in.

_____

8.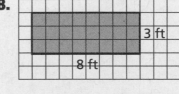

3 ft

8 ft

_____

Name _____ Date _____

Homework Practice

Measurement: Area

Find the area of each figure.

1.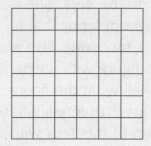

_____

2.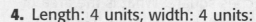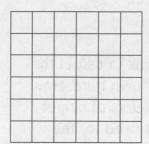

6 mm

25 mm

_____

Use the grid to draw each of the following squares or rectangles. Tell whether the figure is a *square* or *rectangle*. Then find the area.

3. Length: 6 units; width: 2 units:

4. Length: 4 units; width: 4 units:

_____

_____

Spiral Review
Solve. Use the *solve a simpler problem* strategy. (Lesson 11–4)

5. Maria found a store that sells handmade sweaters for $37. She wants to buy one for everyone in her family. She will buy 6 sweaters. How much will this cost? _____

6. James took a job delivering groceries in his neighborhood. He can carry 8 bags with each trip. If he takes 28 trips a day, how many bags does he deliver? _____

7. There are 32 students in Marissa's class. Each student started the year with 15 pencils. How many pencils did the class start with?

_____

Name _____ Date _____

Problem-Solving Practice

Measurement: Area

Find the area of each figure.

1. Lin and her sister are getting a new rug for their bedroom. The rug is 3 feet wide and 5 feet long. Find the area of the rug. _____

2. Lin wants to use blue tissue paper to decorate the top of a box that is 4 inches square. What is the area of the piece of tissue paper Lin needs?

_____

3. Ms. Charles wants to carpet the reading nook shown here. How many square meters of carpet will Ms. Charles need for the reading nook? _____

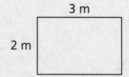

3 m

2 m

4. Helena makes a canvas for an oil painting. Use graph paper to draw the shape of her canvas with length 12 centimeters and width 6 centimeters. Tell what shape Helena's canvas is, and find the area.

_____

5. Mike's sister wants to make a cover for the gas grill on the deck. She has a piece of waterproof fabric that is 4 feet long and 1 foot wide. Use graph paper to draw a figure with length 4 ft and width 1 ft. Tell what the figure is, and find the area. Then tell what shape the section of the deck with the gas grill is and find the area. Will the piece of waterproof fabric cover the grill? _____

_____

_____

_____

_____

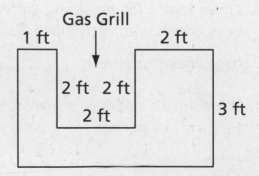

Gas Grill

1 ft   2 ft

2 ft 2 ft

2 ft   3 ft

Name _____ Date _____

Homework Practice

Problem-Solving Investigation: Choose the Best Strategy

Use any strategy shown below to solve.
Tell what strategy you used.

- Reasonable answers
- Act it out
- Guess and check
- Look for a pattern
- Solve a simpler problem

1. A conference center has six rooms. Each room can hold up to 248 people. About how many people can fit in the conference center?

_____

Strategy: _____

2. Ryan's school is going on a field trip. If all six classrooms have 27 students going on the trip, how many students from the

school are going? _____

Strategy: _____

3. Cole has 26 trophies. Julia has eight more than Cole. Eric has seven more than Julia. How many trophies does Eric have?

_____

Strategy: _____

Spiral Review

Find the area of each figure. (Lesson 11–5)

4. 1 yd
3 yd

_____

5.

_____

6. Mrs. Sanchez's room has an area of 1295 square feet. Her room is

35 feet long. How wide is her room? _____

7. Chelsea wants to know the area of the pool deck she scrubs. It is

25 feet wide by 42 feet long. What is the area? _____

Name _____ Date _____

Homework Practice

Measurement: Area of Complex Figures

Find the area of each figure.

1.
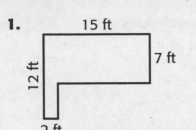
15 ft
7 ft
12 ft
2 ft
_____

2.
16 cm
5 cm
15 cm
20 cm
_____

3.
16 in.
4 in.
10 in.
6 in.
_____

4.
10 in.
18 in.
2 in.
2 in.
_____

5.
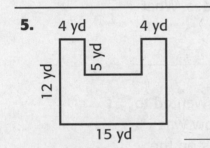
4 yd   4 yd
5 yd
12 yd
15 yd
_____

6.
6 ft
2 ft
7 ft
14 ft
_____

Spiral Review   Use any strategy shown below to solve.
Tell what strategy you used. (Lesson 11–6)

- Reasonable answers
- Act it out

- Guess and check
- Look for a pattern
- Solve a simpler problem

7. My school has 17 classrooms. Each room can hold up to 35 students. How many students can come to my school?

_____ Strategy: _____

_____

8. Justin walks 16 dogs a day. Is it reasonable to say that he walks about 100 dogs in a week? _____ Strategy: _____

_____

Name _____ Date _____

Problem-Solving Practice

Measurement: Area of Complex Figures

Find the area of each figure.

1. Amanda needs to wrap a gift. The box she has to wrap has 6 sides that are each 4 inches × 4 inches. How much paper does she need to wrap this box?

   _____

2. Tony's family wants to figure out how big an area of their home is. They discovered they have a large room that is 20 feet × 17 feet and a room that is 12 feet × 15 feet. How large is this area of their home?

   _____

3. Rosa placed a box that is 25 inches × 36 inches on a table. She discovered that the table is exactly 1 inch larger on all sides. What is the area of the table's top?

   _____

4. Patrick broke his neighbor's window with a baseball. He wanted to find out how much it would cost to replace it. The window was 27 inches × 34 inches on top and 27 inches × 16 inches on the bottom. The store charges 10¢ per square inch for the glass. How much will the glass cost?

   _____

5. Emily is helping wallpaper her bathroom. She has a 3 feet × 5 feet wall and a 2 feet × 8 feet area to cover. How much wallpaper does she need?

   _____

6. Dan has to figure out how much fertilizer he needs for his lawn. His front lawn is 35 feet × 17 feet. His side lawn is 9 feet × 17 feet. His back lawn is 35 feet × 12 feet. How large is his lawn?

   _____

Name _____ Date _____

Homework Practice

Negative Numbers

Write the number that represents each situation. Then show the number on a number line.

1. 75 feet above sea level _____

2. owe $18 _____

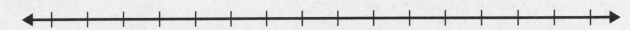

3. 2 feet behind _____

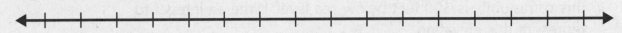

4. reduced by 7 pounds _____

Write the number of each letter on the number line.

5.
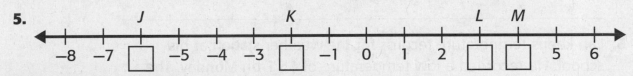

J   K   L   M

-8 -7 ☐ -5 -4 -3 ☐ -1 0 1 2 ☐ ☐ 5 6

Spiral Review

Find the area of each figure. (Lesson 11-7)

6.
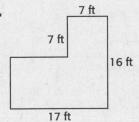

7 ft
7 ft
16 ft
17 ft

_____

7.
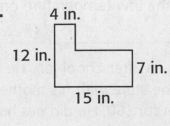

4 in.
12 in.
7 in.
15 in.

Problem-Solving Practice

4NS1.8

Negative Numbers

Solve.

1. Frederico located −5 on a number line. Marge located the opposite. What number did Marge locate?

   _____

2. The temperature on a cold day in Columbus, Ohio, is four degrees below zero. Where would this temperature be found on a number line?

   _____

   _____

3. Valerie lives in a small community in California. The elevation of this community is 300 feet below sea level. Write an integer to represent this elevation.

   _____

4. Simon lives in a cold climate. He measures the low temperatures for one week. These temperatures are 0°F, −2°F, 1°F, 4°F, −6°F, −7°F, and 2°F. Write these numbers from least to greatest.

   _____

   _____

5. Lan keeps temperature records for the weather station at his school. He recorded a low temperature of 15°F on Monday. The low temperature on Tuesday was seven degrees lower than the low temperature on Monday. The low temperature on Wednesday was ten degrees less than the temperature on Tuesday. Use a number line to find the low temperature on Wednesday.

   _____

6. Adam earned $45 at an afterschool job. He received an allowance of $10. He went to the store with his mother and wanted to purchase a CD player for $60. He did not have his money with him, so his mother loaned him enough to make his purchase. He will pay her back. Write an integer to represent the amount of money Adam had to borrow.

   _____

Name _____ Date _____

Homework Practice

Find Points on a Grid

4MG2.1

Identify the object or letter that is located at each ordered pair.

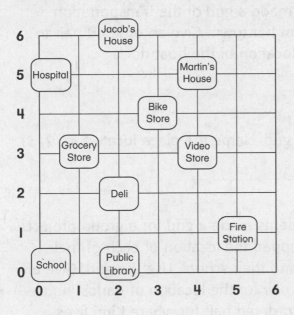

1. (2, 2) _____

2. (3, 4) _____

3. (0, 5) _____

4. (5, 1) _____

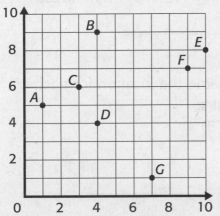

5. (3, 6) _____

6. (10, 8) _____

7. (4, 9) _____

8. (7, 1) _____

Spiral Review   **Write the number that represents each situation. Then show the number on a number line. (Lesson 12-1)**

9. ran 100 yards _____

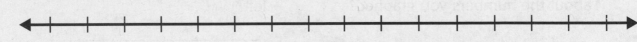

10. earns $8 _____

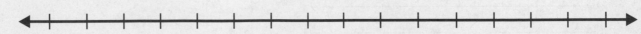

Problem-Solving Practice

4MG2.1

Find Points on a Grid

Use the grids to solve.

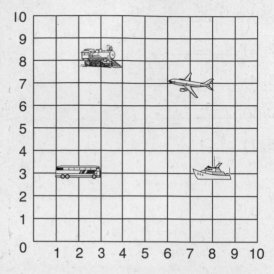

1. Lindsay made a grid of the transportation centers in her town. Give an ordered pair to tell the location of the boat dock.

_____

2. Use the grid. Name the place located at (2, 3).

_____

3. Five students made a grid for a group project. They mapped the location of each of their homes and their school. Use the grid. Give an ordered pair for the location of Carlos' house. Give an ordered pair for where Kimi lives.

_____

4. Use the grid to name the location for each of these ordered pairs:
(2, 2); (6, 4); (1, 8)

_____

Make a grid on a separate sheet of paper to solve.

5. Graph these ordered pairs on graph paper: (3, 2); (4, 4); (5, 2); (5, 7); (6, 4); (7, 2). What do you notice about the numbers you graphed?

_____

_____

_____

6. If each grid line stands for 10 feet, how far is it from the lowest point on the right to the lowest point on the left?

_____

_____

Name _____ Date _____

Homework Practice

Graph Ordered Pairs

Graph and label each point on the grid.

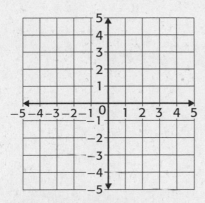

1. point *G*: (4, −5)

2. point *H*: (−2, 2)

3. point *I*: (2, 3)

4. point *J*: (−4, −4)

5. point *K*: (1, 0)

6. point *L*: (−1, 5)

Find the length of the horizontal or vertical line segment formed by each set of ordered pairs.

7. (2, 4), (2, −2) _____

8. (4, 6), (2, 6) _____

Spiral Review

Write the ordered pair that names each point. (Lesson 12-2)

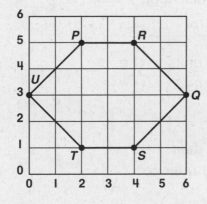

9. *Q* _____

10. *R* _____

11. *S* _____

12. *U* _____

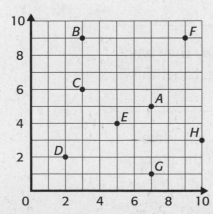

13. *B* _____

14. *H* _____

15. *E* _____

16. *C* _____

Name _____ Date _____

Problem-Solving Practice

Graph Ordered Pairs

Solve.

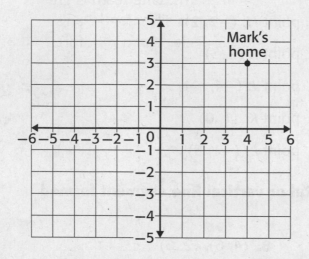

1. Mark went to the left 8 units and down 3 units to the library. Label

   this point. _____

2. Then he went to the right 5 units and down 3 units to school.

   Label this point. _____

3. After school, Mark went to the right 3 units and up 5 units to the
   basketball courts. Label this point.

   _____

4. After basketball, Mark went home with Jane to finish their
   homework. They walked to the right 2 units and up 3 units to
   Jane's house. Label this point.

   _____

5. Mark's mother picked him up, and they went to dinner. They went
   to the left 9 units and down 3 units to the pizza place. Label this

   point. _____

6. Mark's mother had to stop at the grocery store while they were
   out. They went to the left 3 units and down 6 units to the grocery

   store. Label this point. _____

Name _____ Date _____

Homework Practice

Problem-Solving Strategy

Logical Reasoning
Solve. Use the *logical reasoning* strategy.

1. Kristen, Josh, and Dan all play on soccer teams. One team is green, one is blue, and one is silver. Kristen's team is silver, and Dan's team is not green. What color team does each person play for?

_____

_____

_____

2. Jasmine, Courtney, Taylor, and Inez are all on the same basketball team. Their jersey numbers are 4, 5, 8, 11. Inez's number equals the number of letters in her name. Jasmine's number is a two-digit number. Courtney's number is not a prime. What is Taylor's

number? _____

3. Three labrador retrievers play at the park. One is yellow, one is black, and one is chocolate. Their names are Emma, Newton, and Sheldon. Sheldon is not yellow. The black dog's name is the shortest. What are the colors of each dog?

_____

_____

_____

Spiral Review
(Lesson 12-3)

Graph and label each point on the grid.

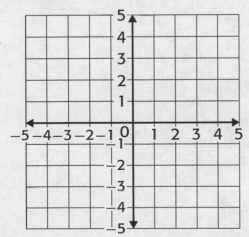

4. point A: (3, −5)

5. point B: (−1, 3)

6. point C: (2, 5)

7. point D: (−5, −3)

8. point E: (2, 0)

9. point F: (−3, 5)

12–5

Homework Practice

Functions

4AF1.5

Complete each function table.

1.

Rule: multiply 4	
Input (x)	Output (y)
0	0
2	8
5	
6	
8	

3.

Rule: $x + x = y$	
Input (x)	Output (y)
0	0
2	4
7	
9	
12	

2.

Rule: $2x + 1 = y$	
Input (x)	Output (y)
1	3
3	7
5	
7	
9	

4.

Rule: $x \div 3 + 6 = y$	
Input (x)	Output (y)
0	6
3	7
6	
9	
12	

Spiral Review

Solve. Use the *logical reasoning* strategy. (Lesson 12-4)

5. Katherine watches the neighborhood children as they learn to ride their bikes. Some ride with training wheels, others do not. If there are 5 children riding their bikes, and there are 16 wheels, how many are riding with and without training wheels?

_____

_____

Name _____ Date _____

Problem-Solving Practice

4AF1.5

Functions

Solve.

1. A falcon flies 3 times as fast as a hummingbird. Complete the function table. Write an equation for the function table.

h	1	2	3	4	5
f	3	6			

2. For every instrument in the band room, there are 4 students learning to play it. Complete the function table to show this. Then write an equation for the function table.

i	1	2	3	4	5
s					

3. For every hour of homework, Maya plays for 2 hours. Complete the function table to show Maya's schedule. Then write an equation for the function table.

h	1	2	3	4	5
p					

4. Milo is making brownies. For every tablespoon of water, he adds 5 teaspoons of flour. Make a function table showing this. Then write an equation for the function table.

w	1	2	3	4	5
f					

5. Each house number is 2 less than 4 times the number of the house next door. Make a function table showing this. Then write an equation for the function table.

n	1	2	3	4	5
h					

6. Rey is playing a game. For every 2 steps forward he takes, he takes one step back. Complete the function table to show Rey's steps. Then write an equation for the function table.

f	2	4	6	8	10
b					

178

Homework Practice

Graph Functions

Graph ten points on the graph of the function.

1. $y = 2x + 2$

2. $y = 7$

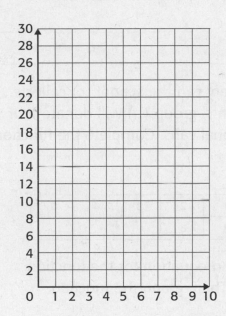

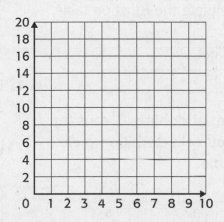

_____

_____

_____

_____

_____

_____

Spiral Review
(Lesson 12-5)

Copy and complete each function table.

3.

Rule: $x - 5 = y$	
Input (x)	Output (y)
5	0
9	4
12	
15	
18	

4.

Rule: $x + 1 = y$	
Input (x)	Output (y)
2	3
5	6
10	
12	
17	

Name _____ Date _____

Problem-Solving Practice

Graph Functions

Solve. Graph the functions where indicated on another piece of paper.

1. In a school food drive, Foodmart (f) will donate 1 can for every 2 cans (c) purchased. Complete the function table.

f	1	2	3	4	5
c	2	4	6		

2. Write an equation for the function table. Then, graph the function.

_____

_____

3. Suppose Foodmart donates 3 cans for each can of food collected. Complete the function table.

c	1	2	3	4	5
f	3	6	9		

Write an equation for the function table. Then, graph the function.

_____

_____

4. For every can the school (c) collects, a parents' group (p) will donate four additional cans. Complete the function table.

c	1	2	3	4	5
p	4	8			

Write an equation for the function table. Then, graph the function.

_____

_____

5. The school (s) also collected blankets. For every 3 blankets donated (d), the school (s) will buy 1 additional blanket. Complete the function table. Then, graph the function.

d	3	6			
s	1	2	3	4	5

_____

_____

6. A town service club (c) agrees to help. This club will match the number of blankets donated (b) and will give one additional blanket as well. Copy and complete the function table. Then, graph the function.

b	1	2	3	4	5
c	2	3			

_____

_____

Name _____ Date _____

Homework Practice

Problem-Solving Investigation

Use any strategy shown below to solve each problem.

- Act it out
- Guess and check
- Look for a pattern
- Solve a simpler problem
- Logical reasoning

1. For every day that everyone in class does his homework, Mrs. Ramirez puts two pebbles in a bowl. When she has 178 pebbles, the students will have no homework. How many days must everyone complete his homework before Mrs. Ramirez assigns no homework? _____

2. Alexis, Danielle, and Victoria each want to make a bracelet from beads. There are blue glass, purple plastic, and yellow clay beads. Alexis uses purple beads. Danielle prefers clay beads. What beads will each girl use? _____

_____

Spiral Review

Graph ten points on the graph of the function. (Lesson 12-6)

3. $y = x + 4$

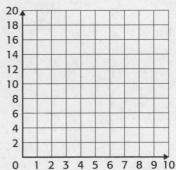

_____

_____

_____

4. $x = 3$

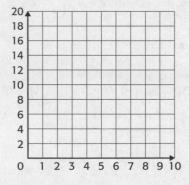

_____

_____

_____

Name _____ Date _____

Homework Practice

Parts of a Whole

Draw a picture and shade part of it to show a fraction.

1. $\frac{1}{2}$ 4. $\frac{3}{5}$ 7. $\frac{2}{3}$

2. $\frac{3}{4}$ 5. $\frac{7}{8}$ 8. $\frac{4}{9}$

3. $\frac{5}{6}$ 6. $\frac{5}{10}$ 9. $\frac{3}{7}$

Solve.

10. A pizza is cut in 8 pieces. Maria ate two of the pieces. Her friends ate the remaining pieces. What fraction of the pizza did Maria eat?

_____

11. A recipe to bake biscuits calls for 2 cups of milk and 4 cups of flour. What fraction of the ingredients is milk?

_____

12. A recipe for crunchy treats calls for 1 cup of chocolate and 3 cups of crunchy cereal. What fraction of the ingredients is chocolate?

_____

Spiral Review   Use any strategy to solve. (Lesson 12–7)

13. Mr. Benson spends $48 on two tickets to the concert. At this rate, how much would 12 tickets cost? _____

14. Marcus downloads 17 songs on his computer. He downloads two additional songs each day for a week. How many more songs does he need to download to have 50 songs? _____

15. Jaclyn has a collection of books. She has two mystery books for every science-fiction book. She has three times as many adventure books as mystery books. Jaclyn has four mystery books. How many science-fiction and adventure books does she have?

_____

_____

13–1

Problem-Solving Practice

Parts of a Whole

4NS1.5

Solve.

1. Tony lost a button off his shirt. He measures one of the remaining buttons to find out what size button to buy to replace the one he lost.

   Find the width of Tony's button and write a fraction for the part of an inch.

   _____

3. Diallo baked a pumpkin pie. He sliced it into 6 pieces. His family ate 5 of the pieces. Write a fraction to show what part of the pie the family ate.

   _____ of a pie

   Write a fraction to show how much of the pie is left.

   _____ of a pie

5. Alani has a pizza that is cut into 8 slices. After she and her friends finish eating, there are 3 slices left. Write a fraction that names the part of the pizza that is left.

   _____ of a pizza

2. Ciro has finished 1 part of his homework assignment. There are 3 parts to the assignment. What fraction of his assignment has he completed?

   Use grid paper to draw a rectangle and shade it to show how much of the assignment Ciro has finished.

   _____

4. Megan has read 4 chapters of a book about electricity. There are 8 chapters in the book. Use grid paper to draw a rectangle and shade it to show how much of the book Megan has read. If she reads two more chapters, what fraction of the book will she have read?

   _____ of the book

6. Jesse has a block of cheddar cheese. He cuts it into 12 equal chunks and puts toothpicks into them to serve at a party. After the party, Jesse discovers that 11 cheese chunks have been eaten. Write a fraction to show what part of the block of cheese was eaten.

   _____ of the cheese

Name _____ Date _____

Homework Practice

Parts of a Set

Draw a picture to show each set.

1. $\frac{3}{4}$ of a set of shapes are circles.

2. $\frac{7}{8}$ of a set of shapes are squares.

3. $\frac{5}{6}$ of a set of shapes are rectangles.

4. $\frac{3}{7}$ of a set of lines are zigzag.

5. $\frac{7}{10}$ of a group of whales are grownups, $\frac{3}{10}$ of the group are babies.

Solve.

6. Miguel's mom brought home a bag of 15 hats for his birthday party. 6 of the hats are pointed shiny red hats. What fraction of the hats are pointed hats?

6. _____

7. The other hats are striped and have bells. What fraction of the 15 hats are striped hats?

7. _____

8. Miguel's mom also has a bag of 16 toys. 9 of the toys are balls. What fraction of toys are balls?

8. _____

9. There are also 7 whistles in the bag of toys. What fraction of 16 toys are whistles?

9. _____

10. The last bag Miguel's mom brought home has 18 noisemakers. Miguel took 3 of the blowers out of the bag and started using them before the party. What fraction of the noisemakers are left for the party guests?

10. _____

Spiral Review Draw a picture and shade part of it to show a fraction. (Lesson 13-1)

11. $\frac{1}{4}$

13. $\frac{5}{9}$

15. $\frac{4}{8}$

12. $\frac{5}{12}$

14. $\frac{3}{6}$

16. $\frac{7}{11}$

17. Look back over the page. Circle every fraction that shows more than one half.

13–2

Problem-Solving Practice

4NS1.5, 4NS1.7

Parts of a Set

Solve.

1. Lara saw 3 snowmen on her way to school. She noticed that 2 of the three snowmen were smiling. On a separate sheet of paper, draw a picture of the snowmen that Lara saw. Then write a fraction that describes the number of snowmen who are smiling.

_____

2. Ali has a group of 9 game pieces. Some of them are white and some of them are not.

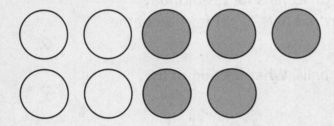

   Write a fraction that shows the part of Ali's game pieces that are white. _____

3. Diane has laid out 12 game cards. She put 7 of the cards face up and 5 of the cards face down. Write a fraction that names the part of Diane's cards that are face up. _____

4. James spends 2 hours a day doing homework. What fraction of the day does James spend on homework? _____

5. There are 8 students in the chess club. Only 7 of the members attended the last meeting. Write a fraction that tells what part of the chess club missed the meeting. _____

6. There are 32 bottles of milk on the grocery store shelf. Carrie buys 5 of the bottles and Heather buys 11 of them. What fraction of the original number of milk bottles is left after Carrie and Heather make their purchases? _____

Name _____ Date _____

Homework Practice

Problem-Solving Strategy

Solve. Use the *draw a picture* strategy.

1. Janice bought her mother a bunch of 12 flowers. 2 of the flowers are daisies. The others look like big cotton balls. Which flower are there the most of? _____

2. There are 6 books on the table. $\frac{1}{2}$ of them are reading books. 1 of them is a math book and the rest are science books. How many are science books? _____

3. Mrs. Jones has 6 pine trees in her backyard. The tree closest to the house is $\frac{1}{2}$ as tall as the trees against the fence. The height of each of the 5 trees against the fence is 12 feet. How tall is the tree near the house? _____

4. Marty's friend Eugene lives 3 streets north of Marty's street. Marty walked over to Eugene's street and together they walked to school. The school is 6 streets to the east of Eugene's street. What directions can the boys follow to return to Marty's street?

_____

Spiral Review   Draw a picture to show each set.

(Lesson 13-2)

5. $\frac{5}{6}$ of a set of shapes are rectangles.

6. $\frac{3}{7}$ of a set of lines are zigzag.

7. $\frac{7}{10}$ of a group of elephants are grownups, $\frac{3}{10}$ of the group are babies.

Solve.

8. Andrew's dad brought home a group of 25 parts to build boxcars. 4 of the parts are steering wheels. What fraction of the parts are steering wheels? _____

9. Andrew's dad also had 16 small tires. What fraction of the group of 25 parts are tires? _____

Name _____ Date _____

Homework Practice

Equivalent Fractions

Find an equivalent fraction for each fraction.

1. $\frac{3}{4}$ _____

2. $\frac{3}{5}$ _____

3. $\frac{2}{5}$ _____

4. $\frac{4}{6}$ _____

5. $\frac{6}{12}$ _____

6. $\frac{8}{16}$ _____

7. $\frac{7}{8}$ _____

8. $\frac{3}{9}$ _____

Solve.

9. A Ferris wheel has 10 seats. 5 of the seats are red. Write two fractions that describe the part of the cars that are red.

_____

Spiral Review

Solve. Use the *draw a picture* strategy. (Lesson 13-3)

10. There are 16 dolphins in the aquarium. $\frac{1}{2}$ are fully trained. 3 are in training. The rest will be trained in the spring. How many dolphins will be trained in the spring?

_____

11. The bus that brings Lisa to school stops 12 times. $\frac{1}{3}$ of the stops are made before the bus gets to Lisa. After the bus stops to pick up Lisa, how many more stops are there?

_____

12. Look back over the page and circle every fraction that is equal to one half.

Name _____ Date _____

Problem-Solving Practice

Equivalent Fractions

Solve.

1. Ms. Andrews has an umbrella that is gray and white. Look at the top of her umbrella.

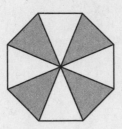

What fractional part of the umbrella is gray?

_____

Write an equivalent fraction.

_____

_____

_____

2. Dean has 10 marbles. He gives 2 of them to Jamie. Write a fraction for the number of marbles Dean has left.

_____

3. Lainie delivers newspapers. She spends $\frac{4}{12}$ of her earnings on a new CD. Write an equivalent fraction to show the amount of Lainie's earnings that she spends.

_____

_____

4. There are 32 students in Mr. Simon's class. Four of the students are on the soccer team. Write the fraction that shows how many of Mr. Simon's students are on the team.

_____

5. Ms. Ashton's class set 9 major goals for their school year. They have reached 6 of their goals. Write a fraction that names the goals that have been reached.

_____

Then write 2 equivalent fractions.

_____

_____

6. There are 72 players in the soccer league and 54 of the players are new this year. Write a fraction that shows the number of players who are new this year.

_____

Homework Practice

Simplest Form

Write each fraction in simplest form. If it is in simplest form, write *simplest form*.

1. $\frac{3}{9}$ _____

2. $\frac{5}{15}$ _____

3. $\frac{1}{3}$ _____

4. $\frac{24}{36}$ _____

5. $\frac{7}{35}$ _____

6. $\frac{6}{48}$ _____

7. $\frac{20}{25}$ _____

8. $\frac{7}{49}$ _____

9. $\frac{15}{30}$ _____

10. $\frac{16}{40}$ _____

ALGEBRA Find the value of *x* to simplify each fraction.

11. $\frac{9}{27} = \frac{x}{3}$ _____

12. $\frac{7}{63} = \frac{x}{9}$ _____

13. $\frac{15}{50} = \frac{3}{x}$ _____

Write as a fraction in simplest form.

14. Six of the 12 muffins in a bag are blueberry. What fraction of

muffins are blueberry? _____

Spiral Review Find an equivalent fraction for each fraction. (Lesson 13-4)

15. $\frac{9}{18}$ _____

16. $\frac{6}{16}$ _____

17. $\frac{12}{18}$ _____

18. $\frac{2}{6}$ _____

19. $\frac{5}{20}$ _____

20. $\frac{3}{9}$ _____

21. $\frac{4}{28}$ _____

22. $\frac{4}{8}$ _____

Name _____ Date _____

Problem-Solving Practice

Simplest Form

Solve.

1. Ryan has 8 kittens. 2 of the kittens are white. Write a fraction for the number of kittens Ryan has that are not white in simplest form.

   _____

2. Laura has 10 marbles. After she gives 2 of them to Emma, she has $\frac{8}{10}$ of her marbles left. Write a fraction for the number of marbles Laura gave away in simplest form.

   _____

3. Aidan likes to build with his 12 blocks. He used 8 blocks to build a house. Write a fraction in simplest form that tells what fraction of Aidan's blocks were used in the house.

   _____

4. Ellen has 6 cousins. 2 of her cousins live nearby. Write a fraction for the number of cousins that do not live near Ellen in simplest form.

   _____

5. Nick wants to run 9 miles in a week. So far he has run 3 miles. Write a fraction in simplest form that names how many Nick has run.

   _____

Name _____ Date _____

Homework Practice

Problem-Solving Investigation

4MR2.2, 4NS1.7

Choose a Strategy

Use any strategy shown below to solve.

- Use Logical Reasoning
- Look for a Pattern
- Solve a Simpler Problem
- Guess and Check
- Draw a Picture

1. Mark has some coins. He has 2 more quarters than nickels and 4 more dimes than quarters. If he has 6 nickels, how much money does he have? _____

2. Jerry owns 30 sports posters. $\frac{1}{2}$ of them are small posters. $\frac{1}{3}$ are medium posters. The rest are large posters. How many are large posters? _____

3. Linda bought 5 new jerseys. The long sleeved ones cost $15, and the striped ones cost $10. She spent a total of $60. How many of each type of shirt did she buy?

_____

Spiral Review

Write each fraction in simplest form. If it is in simplest form, write *simplest form*. (Lesson 13-5)

4. $\frac{10}{20}$ _____

5. $\frac{42}{54}$ _____

6. $\frac{14}{28}$ _____

7. $\frac{3}{21}$ _____

8. $\frac{8}{40}$ _____

9. $\frac{28}{49}$ _____

10. $\frac{24}{32}$ _____

11. $\frac{15}{30}$ _____

12. $\frac{7}{10}$ _____

13. $\frac{18}{81}$ _____

14. $\frac{25}{55}$ _____

15. $\frac{3}{4}$ _____

ALGEBRA Find the value of x to simplify each fraction.

16. $\frac{8}{56} = \frac{X}{7}$ ___

17. $\frac{6}{9} = \frac{X}{3}$ ___

18. $\frac{6}{54} = \frac{X}{9}$ ___

19. $\frac{16}{20} = \frac{X}{5}$ ___

Homework Practice

Problem-Solving Investigation

Choose a Strategy

Use any strategy shown below to solve.

- Use Logical Reasoning
- Look for a Pattern
- Solve a Simpler Problem
- Guess and Check
- Draw a Picture

1. Mark has some coins. He has 2 more quarters than nickels and 4 more dimes than quarters. If he has 6 nickels, how much money does he have?

2. Jerry owns 30 sports posters. 1/3 of them are small posters. 4/15 are medium posters. The rest are large posters. How many are large posters?

3. Linda bought 3 new jerseys. Two long sleeved ones cost $12 and the short sleeved ones cost $10. She spent a total of $50. How many of each type of shirt did she buy?

Spiral Review Write each fraction in simplest form. If it is in simplest form, write simplest form. (Lesson 13-4)

ALGEBRA Find the value of x to simplify each fraction.

Name _____ Date _____

Homework Practice

Compare and Order Fractions

Compare. Write >, <, or =.

1. $\frac{1}{4}$ ◯ $\frac{2}{4}$ 5. $\frac{5}{6}$ ◯ $\frac{3}{12}$ 9. $\frac{8}{12}$ ◯ $\frac{1}{3}$

2. $\frac{2}{5}$ ◯ $\frac{2}{3}$ 6. $\frac{4}{6}$ ◯ $\frac{5}{9}$ 10. $\frac{7}{7}$ ◯ $\frac{9}{9}$

3. $\frac{5}{10}$ ◯ $\frac{4}{8}$ 7. $\frac{2}{9}$ ◯ $\frac{1}{8}$

4. $\frac{6}{12}$ ◯ $\frac{3}{4}$ 8. $\frac{4}{5}$ ◯ $\frac{8}{10}$

Order from *least* to *greatest*.

11. $\frac{5}{10}, \frac{8}{12}, \frac{1}{3}$ ____, ____, ____   13. $\frac{4}{9}, \frac{7}{11}, \frac{2}{8}$ ____, ____, ____

12. $\frac{1}{3}, \frac{8}{1}, \frac{5}{11}$ ____, ____, ____

Solve.

14. Joe worked on his woodworking project for $\frac{3}{4}$ of an hour Monday evening. Tuesday evening, he worked for $\frac{7}{8}$ of an hour. Which day did he work longer? _____

Spiral Review   Use any strategy shown below to solve. (Lesson 13-6)

- Use logical reasoning
- Solve a simpler problem
- Draw a picture
- Look for a pattern
- Guess and check

15. Jack and Frank shared the cost of renting a boat. It cost $20 an hour and they used it 5 hours. How much did each friend pay?

_____

16. Janice leaves to walk to her friend's house at 3:30. She arrives at her friend's house at 3:45. How many minutes did it take her to walk to her friend's? _____

17. Look back over the page and circle all the fractions with a denominator of 9.

13-7

Problem-Solving Practice

Compare and Order Fractions

4NS1.9

Solve.

1. Lon can have $\frac{2}{3}$ cup of orange juice or $\frac{3}{4}$ cup of milk. Which amount is more?

_____

2. Patti has three glue sticks that are partially used. One has $\frac{1}{5}$ left, one has $\frac{3}{5}$ left, and one has $\frac{3}{10}$ left. Order the fractions from *least* to *greatest*.

_____

3. Eduardo has three cans of paint. One can is $\frac{3}{8}$ full, one is $\frac{3}{4}$ full, and one is $\frac{2}{16}$ full. Order the cans from *greatest* to *least* amounts of paint.

_____

4. Samuel is making bread and needs $\frac{5}{8}$ cup of flour. Jason is making a different kind of bread and needs $\frac{3}{4}$ cup of flour. Who needs the greater amount of flour?

_____

5. Lola measures three buttons to find one which will fit the buttonhole on the shirt she is making. One is $\frac{3}{16}$ inch, one is $\frac{3}{8}$ inch, and one is $\frac{1}{4}$ inch. Order the button sizes from *largest* to *smallest*.

_____

6. Jerilyn has finished $\frac{27}{32}$ of her math problems. Matt has finished $\frac{7}{8}$ of his math problems. Who has finished the greatest number of math problems?

_____

13-8

Homework Practice

3NS3.2

Add and Subtract Like Fractions

Find each sum or difference. Write in simplest form.

1. $\dfrac{2}{4} + \dfrac{1}{4} =$ ____

2. $\dfrac{6}{12} - \dfrac{4}{12} =$ ____

3. $\dfrac{3}{10} + \dfrac{2}{10} =$ ____

4. $\dfrac{5}{7} + \dfrac{1}{7} =$ ____

5. $\dfrac{6}{8} - \dfrac{3}{8} =$ ____

6. $\dfrac{4}{9} - \dfrac{4}{9} =$ ____

7. $\dfrac{5}{6} - \dfrac{2}{6} =$ ____

8. $\dfrac{8}{11} + \dfrac{1}{11} =$ ____

9. $\dfrac{4}{12} + \dfrac{3}{12} =$ ____

10. $\dfrac{4}{9} + \dfrac{4}{9} =$ ____

11. $\dfrac{10}{12} - \dfrac{8}{12} =$ ____

12. $\dfrac{8}{15} - \dfrac{5}{15} =$ ____

Solve.

13. Summer watched $\dfrac{3}{6}$ of a movie. Then, she watched another $\dfrac{2}{6}$. What fraction of the movie does she have left to watch?

_____

14. John is hitting baseballs at a batting cage. He used $\dfrac{5}{12}$ of the baseballs the first time he batted. Then, he used $\dfrac{3}{12}$ more. What fraction of the baseballs does he have left?

_____

Spiral Review   **Compare. Write >, <, or =.**
(Lesson 13–7)

15. $\dfrac{3}{4}$ ◯ $\dfrac{2}{4}$ 16. $\dfrac{1}{2}$ ◯ $\dfrac{6}{12}$ 17. $\dfrac{3}{5}$ ◯ $\dfrac{7}{10}$

Order from *least* to *greatest*.

18. $\dfrac{2}{3}, \dfrac{3}{12}, \dfrac{5}{6}$ ____   19. $\dfrac{4}{5}, \dfrac{7}{10}, \dfrac{1}{2}$ ____

20. Look back over the page. Circle all of the fractions with a denominator of 6.

Name _____ Date _____

Problem-Solving Practice

Add and Subtract Like Fractions

Solve. Write the result in simplest form.

1. Sam has a set of 6 wildcat animal cards. The set of cards is made up of $\frac{2}{6}$ tigers, $\frac{1}{6}$ pumas, and $\frac{3}{6}$ lions. If Sam gave away the tiger and puma cards, how many cards would he have left?

   _____

2. Amber sliced a watermelon into 12 wedges. She ate 1 wedge, her brother ate 2 wedges, and her uncle ate 3 wedges. What fraction of the melon did they eat?

   _____

3. There are 8 pieces of fruit in a bowl. If you removed $\frac{1}{4}$ of the fruit, how many pieces would remain?

   _____

4. There are 6 students in a group. One student wrote a science report on animals. One student wrote a science report on trees. Four students wrote social studies reports. What fraction of the group wrote science reports?

   _____

5. Rachel baked a blueberry pie. She ate $\frac{1}{6}$. How much pie is left for her family?

   _____

6. Brice and his younger sister, Carla, share 21 chores each week. They do 3 chores each day. What fraction of the week's chores do Brice and Carla do on 2 days?

   _____

Name _____ Date _____

Homework Practice

4NS1.5, 4NS1.9

Mixed Numbers

Identify the points on the number line below. Write each point as a mixed number.

1. A _____

2. B _____

Identify the points on the number line below. Write each point as an improper fraction.

3. C _____

4. D _____

Write each mixed number as an improper fraction.

5. $2\frac{3}{4}$ _____   **6.** $5\frac{3}{5}$ _____   **7.** $6\frac{2}{3}$ _____

Write each improper fraction as a mixed number.

8. $\frac{15}{2}$ _____   **9.** $\frac{16}{5}$ _____   **10.** $\frac{23}{7}$ _____

Spiral Review   Find each sum or difference. Write in simplest form. (Lesson 13–8)

11. $\frac{1}{4} + \frac{2}{4} =$ _____   **12.** $\frac{3}{9} + \frac{2}{9} =$ _____

13. $\frac{7}{8} - \frac{5}{8} =$ _____   **14.** $\frac{9}{10} - \frac{3}{10} =$ _____

15. $\frac{5}{6} - \frac{2}{6} =$ _____   **16.** $\frac{3}{7} + \frac{3}{7} =$ _____

17. $\frac{3}{5} + \frac{1}{5} =$ _____   **18.** $\frac{11}{12} - \frac{7}{12} =$ _____

Solve.

19. Angie used $\frac{2}{4}$ of the paints in her paint set. Her sister used $\frac{1}{4}$ of Angie's paints. How much of the paints did they use in all? _____

Name _____ Date _____

Problem-Solving Practice

Mixed Numbers

Solve.

1. Ana has 13 crayons that are only $\frac{1}{3}$ as long as they used to be. Rename $\frac{13}{3}$ as a mixed number in simplest form.

   _____

2. Vic needs $1\frac{1}{2}$ cups of flour to bake bread. How many halves is that?

   _____

3. Pedro uses $\frac{1}{9}$ of a sheet of art paper to make one paper crane. He makes 75 cranes. How many sheets of art paper does Pedro use to make the cranes? Rename $\frac{75}{9}$ as a mixed number in simplest form.

   _____

4. Jenny needs $3\frac{2}{3}$ cups of flour to bake bread. How many thirds is that?

   _____

5. The hardware company uses $\frac{1}{8}$ of a roll of wire to make a hook. The company made 338 hooks on Tuesday. How many rolls of wire did they use? Write your answer as a mixed number in simplest form.

   _____

6. Tamika uses $\frac{1}{4}$ of a block of wax to make a candle. How many blocks of wax does she use to make 22 candles? Write your answer as a mixed number in simplest form.

   _____

Name _____ Date _____

Homework Practice

Tenths and Hundredths

Write a fraction and a decimal for each shaded part.

1.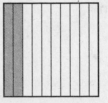

_____

2.

_____

3.

_____

4.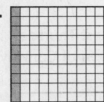

_____

5.

_____

Write the fraction as a decimal.

6. $\frac{3}{10}$ _____

8. $\frac{68}{100}$ _____

10. $\frac{1}{10}$ _____

7. $\frac{45}{100}$ _____

9. $\frac{5}{100}$ _____

Write as a decimal.

11. Marty caught $\frac{4}{10}$ of an inch of rain in his rain gauge. _____

12. $\frac{48}{100}$ of the students were girls. _____

13. thirty-seven hundredths _____

14. twenty-five hundredths _____

15. seven-tenths _____

 **Spiral Review**

Write each as an improper fraction or mixed number. (Lesson 13–9)

16. $4\frac{8}{9}$ _____

17. $\frac{45}{6}$ _____

18. $\frac{37}{5}$ _____

Name _____ Date _____

Problem-Solving Practice

Tenths and Hundredths

Solve.

1. Three-tenths of the students who use the recreation center play in the softball league. What is this fraction as a decimal?

   _____

2. About half of the students who play soccer also play basketball. What is this number as a fraction? As a decimal?

   _____

3. It has been a dry summer in Texas. Last Thursday, nine-hundredths of an inch of rain finally fell in the town of Conway. What is this as a decimal?

   _____

4. Tony spent $\frac{7}{10}$ as much time practicing on his piano as he spent practicing soccer. How much time is that in decimal form?

   _____

5. Last winter, it snowed two and a half inches in the town of Pratt. When the snow melted, the weather station recorded the total precipitation as twenty-three hundredths of an inch. How could they have expressed this as a decimal?

   _____

6. Liam called 10 parks one Sunday. He discovered that 3 of them were being used for soccer matches. What would that be as a fraction?

   _____

   As a decimal?

   _____

   Suppose Liam had called 100 parks. If he discovered $\frac{3}{10}$ of them were being used for soccer matches, how many parks would that be?

   _____ parks

Name _____ Date _____

Homework Practice

Relate Mixed Numbers and Decimals

Write each as a mixed number and decimal.

1.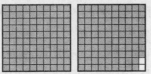

_____ _____

2.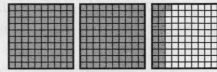

_____ _____

3. two and thirty-one hundredths

_____ _____

4. seventy-eight hundredths

_____ _____

Write each as a decimal.

5. $4\frac{8}{10}$

_____

6. $11\frac{1}{100}$

_____

7. $8\frac{90}{100}$

_____

8. $9\frac{19}{100}$

_____

Spiral Review

Write a fraction and a decimal for each shaded part.

9.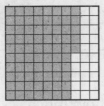

_____

10.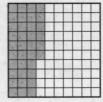

_____

Write as a fraction and as a decimal.

11. twenty-two hundredths

_____

12. sixty-four hundredths

_____

14-2

Problem-Solving Practice

4NS1.6

Solve.

1. The school bell rings for 7 and $\frac{21}{100}$ of a second. What is the decimal form for how long the bell rings?

_____

2. In a speed-skating race, the winning skater's time was $\frac{435}{100}$ seconds faster than the second-place skater. What is the decimal for this fraction?

_____

3. Alan used graph paper to show the length of the ring on his cell phone. If each grid is equal to one second, what is the length of the ring? Write the answer as a mixed number in simplest form and as a decimal.

_____

_____

4. Jana used graph paper to show how many miles it is from her house to school. If each grid is equal to one mile, how far is Jana's house from school?

 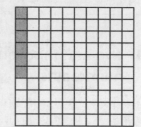

Write the answer as a mixed number and as a decimal.

_____ miles

5. Judy and Trish read that the total rainfall in their town was, "two and thirty-four hundredths of an inch." Judy wrote that fraction as $2\frac{34}{100}$ inches. Trish wrote it as $2\frac{17}{50}$ inches. Who was right? Explain.

_____

_____

_____

_____

Using decimal form, how much rainfall did their town receive?

_____

Name _____ Date _____

Homework Practice

Problem-Solving Strategy: Make a Model

Solve. Use the *make a model* strategy.

1. Manuel makes and sells birdhouses. He uses 7 pieces of wood for each birdhouse and he pays $1.59 for each piece of wood. If he makes a $4.87 profit per birdhouse, how much is he charging for each birdhouse? How much would a larger birdhouse using 12 pieces of wood with the same profit cost?

   _____

2. Marsha collects dolls. She has 18 dolls with brown hair, 14 dolls with black hair, and 4 dolls with blonde hair. What fraction of the dolls have black hair?

   _____

3. You are having a family reunion and 5 dozen people will be attending. If you figure two ears of corn per person, how many ears of corn will you need?

   _____

4. Mark's older brother does lawn care. He charges $22 to mow a lawn up to 500 square feet. For lawns more than 500 square feet, he charges an additional $5 for each 100 additional square feet. How much will it cost to have Mark's brother mow a lawn that is 20 feet long and 25 feet wide? What is the cost for a lawn that is 30 feet long and 30 feet wide?

   _____

Spiral Review   Write each as a mixed number and decimal. (Lesson 14–2)

5. five and nineteen hundredths _____

6. two and forty-five hundredths _____

7. eighty hundredths _____

Name _____ Date _____

Homework Practice

4NS1.2, 4NS1.9

Compare and Order Decimals

Compare. Write >, <, or =.

1. 0.85 ◯ 8.50   **3.** 1.35 ◯ 3.15   **5.** 2.65 ◯ 2.65

2. 5.72 ◯ 57.2   **4.** 0.17 ◯ 0.87   **6.** 8.41 ◯ 8.4

Order from *greatest* to *least*.

7. 0.3, 0.38, 0.31, 0.40   **9.** 1.9, 0.09, 0.19, 1.19

_____, _____, _____, _____   _____, _____, _____, _____

8. 8.2, 0.82, 8.02   **10.** 3.1, 0.13, 0.03, 3.03

_____, _____, _____   _____, _____, _____, _____

Order from *least* to *greatest*.

11. 24.06, 2.41, 24.1, 24.16   **13.** 6.10, 6.01, 6.11, 6.14

_____, _____, _____, _____   _____, _____, _____, _____

12. 4.98, 49.8, 4.08   **14.** 5.05, 5.5, 0.55, 5.15

_____, _____, _____   _____, _____, _____, _____

Spiral Review

Solve. Use the *make a model* strategy. (Lesson 14–3)

15. Amir's high school track is 400 meters. He runs 8,000 meters at the track, four times a week. How many laps around the track does Amir run in one week?

_____

16. Jake is painting his kitchen. The kitchen has 2 walls that are 14 feet long and 10 feet high. If one gallon covers 100 square feet, how many gallons will Jake need to paint his kitchen?

_____

Name _____ Date _____

Problem-Solving Practice

4NS1.2, 4NS1.9

Compare and Order Decimals

1. Enrique averages 6.8 assists per game. Lorena averages 7.2 assists per game. Gilberto averages 5.9 assists per game. Who averages the most assists?

_____

2. Many kids grow an average of 1.4 inches a year. If you grew 2.8 inches and your friend grew 1.2 inches, who grew more? Who was closer to the average amount? How much more did you grow than the average amount?

_____

3. If California received 2.1 inches of rain in January, 2.4 inches of rain in February, and 1.8 inches of rain in March, how much total rain did they receive? List the months in order of the most to least rain.

_____

4. Martina plays tennis for 3.5 hours a day. Jenna plays tennis for 3.75 hours a day, and Marcus plays for 2.8 hours a day. List the number of hours played from greatest to least.

_____

5. Olivia scored an average of 15.8 points a game, James scored an average of 17.1 points, and Joaquin scored an average of

18.4 points per game. Who had the best average? _____

6. Sean played a game of cards in 14.3 minutes. He played a second game in 13.8 minutes. Which game did he play faster?

_____

7. Lauren, Kim, and Jackie each had different heights in centimeters. Compare their heights and list them from the shortest to tallest.

Name	Height (cm)
Lauren	167.64
Kim	152.4
Jackie	161.54

Name _____ Date _____

Homework Practice

Problem-Solving Investigation: Choose a Strategy

Solve using any strategy shown below.

- Use logical reasoning
- Solve a simpler problem
- Make a model
- Draw a picture
- Look for a pattern

1.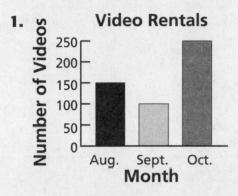

What are the total video sales for August, September, and October?

_____

_____

2. Each morning, Mario walks with his dog. They walk for 1.5 miles. How many miles do they walk in 1 week? How many miles do they walk in 2 weeks?

_____

3. What number comes next in this pattern? What is the rule? 0, 2, 6, 3, 5, 9, 6, 8, _____, _____.

_____

Spiral Review

Compare. Write >, <, or =. (Lesson 14-4)

4. 0.5 ◯ 0.50   **5.** 2.98 ◯ 2.89   **6.** 0.04 ◯ 0.4

Order from *least* to *greatest*.

7. 10.06, 10.16, 10.56, 11.06

_____

8. 5.45, 5.25, 5.05

_____

Name _____ Date _____

Homework Practice

Fraction and Decimal Equivalents

Write a fraction and decimal to describe the shaded part of each model.

1.

_____

_____

3.

_____

_____

2.

_____

_____

4.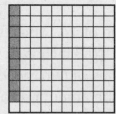

_____

_____

Write each fraction as a decimal.

5. $\frac{77}{100}$ _____ 7. $\frac{12}{100}$ _____ 9. $\frac{1}{4}$ _____

6. $\frac{4}{5}$ _____ 8. $\frac{5}{25}$ _____

Spiral Review

Use any strategy shown below to solve. (Lesson 14-5)

- Look for a pattern
- Solve a simpler problem
- Use logical reasoning
- Draw a picture
- Make a model

10. Nadia's mom gave her $5 for lunch. Her two younger sisters each received $4 for lunch. Nadia's mom had $19 left over. How much

money did she start with? _____

11. What is the rule for the pattern shown? What number comes next?

12, 16, 15, 19, _____

Name _____ Date _____

Problem-Solving Practice

Fraction and Decimal Equivalents

1. Katarina made biscuits. She needed to use $2\frac{1}{4}$ cups of flour for 12 biscuits. If she made 24 biscuits, how much flour did she use written as a decimal?

   _____

2. Louis made a snack with bananas and crackers for his 2 friends and himself. He used 2 bananas and 9 crackers. How much banana did each person get if it was divided evenly? Write your answer as a fraction.

   _____

3. If California received an average of 14.1 inches of rain in 2006, Arizona received an average of 10.8 inches of rain, and Nevada received an average of 9.9 inches of rain, which was the state that received the most rain? Write the amount as a mixed number.

   _____

4. Thomas collects trains. He has 7 blue trains and $\frac{23}{30}$ are other colors. How many trains does Thomas have altogether?

   _____

5. Miriam has 100 buttons in her sewing basket. 28 of them are red, 52 of them are white, 10 are blue, and 10 are black. Write a fraction and a decimal to show how many red and white buttons she has.

   _____

6. There are 52 cards in a deck. $\frac{1}{4}$ of them are hearts, $\frac{1}{4}$ are spades, $\frac{1}{4}$ are diamonds, and $\frac{1}{4}$ are clubs. Write a fraction and decimal to show all the cards that are hearts and diamonds.

   _____

Name _____ Date _____

Homework Practice

Decimals, Fractions, and Mixed Numbers

Compare. Write >, <, or =.

1. 3.05 ◯ $3\frac{11}{100}$ **3.** 0.04 ◯ $\frac{4}{10}$ **5.** $\frac{60}{100}$ ◯ 0.60

2. $\frac{5}{10}$ ◯ 0.49   **4.** 1.35 ◯ $1\frac{3}{10}$ **6.** 9.1 ◯ 9

Order from *greatest* to *least*.

7. 8.45, $8\frac{8}{10}$, 8.81, $8\frac{38}{100}$ **8.** 0.27, $\frac{4}{5}$, 0.52, $\frac{3}{4}$ **9.** 3.2, $2\frac{1}{4}$, 3.19, $2\frac{24}{50}$

_____   _____   _____

_____   _____   _____

_____   _____   _____

_____

Spiral Review

Write a fraction or mixed number and decimal to describe the shaded part of each model. (Lesson 14-6)

10.

_____, _____

11.
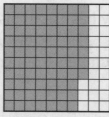

_____, _____

12.

_____, _____

13.
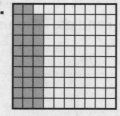

_____, _____

14–7

Problem-Solving Practice

4NS1.9, 4NS1.2

Decimals, Fractions, and Mixed Numbers

Solve.

1. Ana has a crayon that is 2.8 inches long. Monica has a crayon that is $2\frac{3}{4}$ inches long. Who has the longer crayon?

   _____

2. Tori needs $1\frac{1}{2}$ cups of flour to bake bread. Lance needs 1.45 cups of flour. Who needs more flour?

   _____

3. Ramon surveyed 100 students and found $\frac{49}{100}$ of these surveyed like soccer best. $\frac{3}{20}$ of those surveyed like volleyball best, and 0.36 like basketball best. Order the sports from least liked to most liked.

   _____

4. The hardware company has 100 tools. Of the tools $\frac{3}{10}$ are hammers, 0.4 are saws, $\frac{1}{5}$ are screwdrivers and the rest are wrenches. Order the numbers from greatest to least.

   _____

5. Sandy uses $2\frac{1}{4}$ blocks of wax to make candles. Martha uses 2.3 blocks of wax to make candles. Who uses more wax?

   _____

Name _____ Date _____

Homework Practice

4NS2.2

Round Decimals

Round to the nearest *whole number*.

1. 4.39 _____   **3.** 17.42 _____   **5.** 65.32 _____

2. 6.56 _____   **4.** 49.71 _____   **6.** 80.47 _____

Round to the nearest *tenth*.

7. 3.27 _____   **9.** 17.46 _____   **11.** 59.52 _____

8. 8.23 _____   **10.** 32.35 _____   **12.** 71.88 _____

Round to the nearest *whole number*.

13. Nick's largest dog is a Newfoundland. It weighs 156.64 pounds. About how much does Nick's dog weigh? _____

14. Sarah wants to buy a new CD that costs $14.58. About how much money will she need to buy the CD? _____

Spiral Review

Use a number line to compare. Write >, <, or =. (Lesson 14-7)

15. 6.2 ◯ $6\frac{1}{5}$ **16.** 5.4 ◯ $5\frac{1}{3}$ **17.** 3.7 ◯ $3\frac{3}{4}$

Use a number line to order from *greatest* to *least*.

18. $7\frac{1}{2}$; 7.4; $7\frac{7}{8}$; 7.8 _____ _____ _____ _____

19. $8\frac{48}{50}$; 8.15; $8\frac{34}{50}$; 8.77 _____ _____ _____ _____

Write the letter that represents the approximate location of each mixed number or decimal.

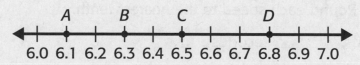

20. $6\frac{4}{8}$ _____   **22.** $6\frac{4}{5}$ _____

21. 6.3 _____   **23.** $6\frac{1}{10}$ _____

Name _____ Date _____

Problem-Solving Practice

Round Decimals

Solve.

1. Jennifer spent 6.34 hours at the beach today. Rounded to the nearest whole hour, how long did she spend at the beach?

    _____

2. In the 1968 Olympics, Mike Burton from the U.S. swam the 400-meter freestyle race in 4.09 seconds. What is his speed rounded to the nearest tenth?

    _____

3. Amy and Kate decide to count the sidewalk squares between their houses. They count exactly 43.34. To the nearest tenth, how many squares are between their houses?

    _____

4. The record for the discus throw at Westlake High School is 30.58 meters. What is this distance rounded to the nearest whole number?

    _____

5. Jon is making a bookshelf unit the exact length of one wall. His measurements show that the wall is 67.07 inches long. If Jon rounds this number to the nearest and cuts pieces of wood that long, how long will each piece of wood be?

    _____

    Will the shelf fit in the room if he does this?

    _____

6. In the 2000 Olympics, Marion Jones from the U.S. ran the 200-meter race in 21.84 seconds. At her track meet, Sara runs it in 32.75 seconds. Round each speed to the nearest tenth.

    _____ seconds, _____ seconds

Homework Practice

Estimate Decimal Sums and Differences

Estimate. Round to the nearest whole number.

1.	6.3	**2.**	3.7	**3.**	8.2	**4.**	17.8
	+ 4.6		+ 5.4		+ 12.5		+ 11.1

**Estimate by rounding to the nearest whole number.
Then compare. Use >, <, or =.**

5. 5.64 + 12.33 ◯ 14.52 + 8.18   **7.** 16.21 − 7.45 ◯ 18.83 − 9.13

6. 9.66 + 9.44 ◯ 13.71 + 5.32   **8.** 17.53 − 5.31 ◯ 15.45 − 6.54

9. Colin is 3.97 feet tall. Caroline is 3.15 feet tall. To the nearest whole number, about how much taller is Colin than Caroline?

_____

10. Ricardo has saved $23.46. Jasmine has saved $18.67. To the nearest dollar, about how much more money has Ricardo saved than Jasmine? _____

Spiral Review

Round to the nearest whole number. (Lesson 15-1)

11. 3.26 ____   **13.** 18.48 _____   **15.** 73.33 _____

12. 7.57 ____   **14.** 53.61 _____   **16.** 88.86 _____

Round to the nearest tenth.

17. 2.13 _____   **19.** 19.34 _____   **21.** 57.53 _____

18. 6.75 _____   **20.** 33.46 _____   **22.** 88.68 _____

Round to the nearest whole number.

23. Jacob works 143.62 hours a year. Emma works 187.34 hours per year. About how many more hours per year does Emma work than Jacob? _____

24. Michelle's family is buying pizza for delivery. It will cost $23.54. About how much money will Michelle's family need? _____

Name _____ Date _____

Problem-Solving Practice

Estimate Decimal Sums and Differences

Estimate. Round to the nearest whole number.

1. The train trip from New York, NY, to Washington, D.C., takes 3.4 hours. The trip from New York to Norfolk, VA, takes 7.6 hours. About how much longer does it take to get to Norfolk?

_____

2. Mr. Jones needs a bag of fertilizer and a bag of pine chips for his garden. A bag of fertilizer costs $8.98 and a bag of pine chips costs $5.13 at the garden store. About how much will Mr. Jones pay?

_____

3. Ellie wants to practice skating in a straight line. She chalks a line on the sidewalk that is 15.75 meters long. Then she adds another 14.25 meters to her line. About how long is Ellie's line now?

_____

4. Nadya has picked up $15.25 worth of art supplies at the hobby store. She puts back a sketch pad that costs $4.98. About how much money will the items cost now?

_____

5. Jeannie wants to buy a jacket that costs $26.83. Her mother agrees to pay $15.50 of the total amount. About how much money does Jeannie need to buy the jacket?

_____

6. Roger spent $43.07 on materials to build a small skate ramp. He spent $76.83 on materials to build a large skate ramp. About how much did Roger spend on the skate ramps altogether?

_____

15–3

Homework Practice

Problem-Solving Strategy

4MR1.1, 4NS3.1

Solve. Use the *work backward* strategy.

1. A number is divided by 4. Then 2 is added to the quotient. Finally the sum is multiplied by 3. The result is 12. What is the number?

   _____

2. Mrs. Washington can jog one mile in 9 minutes. She can walk one mile in 15 minutes. She always stretches for five minutes before exercising. She jogged 2 miles and walked 2 miles. If she finished at 9:15 A.M., what time did she start? _____

3. Alejandro has 4 times as many crayons as markers. He has 6 more markers than pencils. He has 12 pencils. How many crayons does he have? _____

4. Emily bought a $5 sandwich. She then repaid her friend $6. Now Emily has $8. How much money did she have originally? _____

Spiral Review

Estimate. Round to the nearest whole number. (Lesson 15-2)

5.	5.4	6.	2.8	7.	9.3
	+ 5.7		+ 7.3		+ 13.6

Estimate by rounding to the nearest whole number. Then compare. Use >, <, or =.

8. $6.72 + 11.54 \bigcirc 13.33 + 9.44$

9. $8.75 + 11.23 \bigcirc 14.16 + 5.89$

10. $18.46 - 8.29 \bigcirc 14.95 - 5.26$

11. Juan can throw a ball 23.47 yards. Michael can throw a ball 19.77 yards. To the nearest whole number, about how much farther can Juan throw the ball than Michael? _____

12. Sydney can run a mile in 8.6 minutes. Melissa can run a mile in 7.4 minutes. To the nearest whole minute, about how much faster can Melissa run a mile than Sydney? _____

Name _____ Date _____

Homework Practice

Add Decimals

Add.

1. 0.5
   + 0.3
   ‾‾‾‾‾

2. 4.3
   + 5.42
   ‾‾‾‾‾

3. $9.32
   + 4.98
   ‾‾‾‾‾

4. 0.9
   + 0.7
   ‾‾‾‾‾

5. 0.78
   + 8.56
   ‾‾‾‾‾

6. $12.61
   +   6.50
   ‾‾‾‾‾

7. 1.5
   + 0.7
   ‾‾‾‾‾

8. 11.47
   +10.78
   ‾‾‾‾‾

9. $13.01
   + 5.12
   ‾‾‾‾‾

10. 42.31 + 8.77 _____

11. 6.4 + 4.2 + 2.7 _____

12. 52.89 + 48.24 _____

13. 4.2 + 3.33 + 8.1 _____

14. $46.75 + $17.17 _____

15. 7.1 + 2.54 + 3.48 _____

Spiral Review

Solve. Use the *work backward* strategy. (Lesson 15-3)

16. A number is multiplied by 4. Then 7 is subtracted from the product. Finally the result is divided by 3. The result is 7. What is the number?

_____

17. Pedro took 15 minutes to walk home. He played basketball for 30 minutes. Then he ate a snack for 20 minutes. Finally he sat down to start his homework at 4:00 P.M. What time did he leave school?

_____

18. Marissa has 5 times as many pairs of socks as DVDs. She has 4 more DVDs than computer games. She has half as many computer games as baseball caps. If she has 6 baseball caps, how many pairs of socks does she have? _____

15-4

Problem-Solving Practice

Add Decimals

4NS2.1, 4MR2.1

Solve.

1. Talia walked 0.36 miles to the store. Then she walked 2.3 more miles to her grandmother's house. How many miles did she walk in all? _____

2. A small puzzle costs $2.06. A large puzzle costs $3.21. How much would you pay for both puzzles? _____

3. Iris wants to buy a model airplane kit that costs $6.29. She also wants to buy a model car kit that costs $3.89. How much will she pay for both model kits?

   _____

4. A ribbon company produces 31.46 meters of silk ribbon per hour and 2.19 meters of velvet ribbon per hour. In all, how many meters of ribbon do they produce in an hour?

   _____

5. The Winters family is going to a museum. It costs $0.90 for a round-trip bus ticket. It costs $8.75 for a monthly bus pass. Mr. Winters buys a monthly bus pass into the city for himself and his wife because they use them to go to work. He buys his two children round-trip tickets for that day. How much did he pay for his bus tickets?

   _____

6. On Monday, Ms. Tipton braided 7.32 yards of material for a handmade rug during her regular work hours. She braided another 0.97 yard when she worked an hour of overtime. How much material did she braid on Monday?

   _____

Name _____ Date _____

Homework Practice

Problem-Solving Investigation

**Use any strategy shown below to solve.
Tell what strategy you used.**

- Solve a simpler problem
- Use logical reasoning
- Draw a picture
- Make a model
- Work backward

1. Eric buys a ticket to the basketball game for $15. The bus fare to the game and home is $3.50. Snacks at the game cost $6.37. If Eric has $30, how much change will Eric have when he comes home? _____

Strategy:

_____

2. Drew spent 20 minutes completing his reading homework. He spent twice as long on science homework. He spent 10 minutes less on his math homework than he did on his science homework. How long did he spend on all of his homework?

_____

Strategy:

_____

Spiral Review

Add. (Lesson 15–4)

3. $\begin{array}{r} 0.4 \\ + 0.2 \\ \hline \end{array}$

4. $\begin{array}{r} 1.8 \\ + 0.4 \\ \hline \end{array}$

5. $\begin{array}{r} 0.56 \\ + 7.43 \\ \hline \end{array}$

6. $\begin{array}{r} 0.8 \\ + 0.5 \\ \hline \end{array}$

7. $\begin{array}{r} 3.7 \\ + 6.37 \\ \hline \end{array}$

8. $\begin{array}{r} 13.28 \\ + 11.12 \\ \hline \end{array}$

9. $39.62 + 7.24$ _____

10. $\$37.53 + \$18.64$ _____

11. $53.71 + 33.87$ _____

12. $5.3 + 3.8 + 1.9$ _____

Name _____ Date _____

Homework Practice

Subtract Decimals

Subtract.

1. 3.6
    − 2.3

5. 8.22
    − 4.49

9. 19.65
    − 13.42

2. 4.2
    − 1.6

6. $8.15
    − 5.81

10. $21.07
    − 14.19

3. 5.4
    − 4.8

7. 12.32
    − 9.76

11. 41.26
    − 19.72

4. 6.9
    − 2.54

8. $15.76
    − 11.38

12. 55.55
    − 22.66

Spiral Review (Lesson 15–5)

**Use any strategy shown below to solve.
Tell what strategy you used.**

- Use logical reasoning
- Make a model
- Solve a simpler problem
- Draw a picture
- Work backward

13. Cody earns money selling lemonade. He earned $14.55 the first week, $11.75 the second week, $18.54 the last week. How much money did he make selling lemonade? _____

    Strategy: _____

14. Samantha has 15 packages of 12 plates. How many plates does she have? _____

    Strategy: _____

Name _____ Date _____

Problem-Solving Practice

Subtract Decimals

Solve.

1. Petra has $1.78 in her pocket. She spends $0.25 on a banana. How much money does she have left?

   _____

2. Abu weighs his book bag. It weighs 11.65 pounds. He takes out the dictionary and weighs it. The dictionary weighs 3.31 pounds. If he leaves the dictionary out, how much will the book bag weigh?

   _____

3. Celia has $16.41 saved. She wants to buy a book that costs $8.56. If she buys the book, how much money will she have left?

   _____

4. Andrea buys a roll of ribbon that is 13.85 meters long. She needs 2.9 meters of ribbon to decorate a picture frame. How much ribbon will she have left?

   _____

5. The computer game that Parker wants to buy costs $21.07 with tax. He has $17.86. How much more money does he need to buy the game?

   _____

6. Clarissa uses 12.06 meters of string to weave a big bag. She uses 9.14 meters of string to weave a smaller bag. How much more string does she use for the big bag?

   _____

Name _____ Date _____

Homework Practice

Probability and Outcomes

Describe the probability of each outcome. Use *certain*, *likely*, *equally likely*, *unlikely*, or *impossible*.

1. Spinning an even number _____

2. Spinning a 2 _____

3. Spinning a 4, 5, or 6 _____

4. Spinning a 7 _____

5. Spinning a 1, 2, 3, 4, 5, or 6 _____

Create a table to show the possible outcomes for the situation. Then, use the table to describe the probability of the outcome.

6. Jorge is picking something for dinner. He has 2 boxes of pasta, 3 boxes of rice, and 5 types of meat. If he picks one randomly, describe the probability of picking a meat.

_____

 Review

Subtract. (Lesson 15–6)

7.   13.87
      − 6.42
      _____

8.   21.66
      −13.56
      _____

9.   18.04
      − 9.75
      _____

10. $8.99
      − 3.15
      _____

11. $16.05
      − 7.33
      _____

12. $12.50
      − 9.95
      _____

Name _____ Date _____

Problem-Solving Practice

Probability and Outcomes

Describe the probability of each outcome. Use *certain*, *likely*, *equally likely*, *unlikely*, or *impossible*.

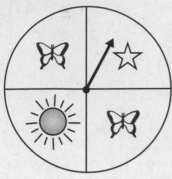

1. spinning a star or a sun

_____

2. spinning a butterfly

_____

3. spinning a baseball or bat

_____

4. spinning a catcher's mitt

_____

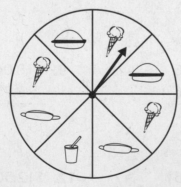

5. spinning a hot dog or a hamburger

_____

6. probability of spinning a soda

_____

228

Name _____ Date _____

Homework Practice

4SDAP2.2

Probability and Fractions

A shape is picked from the bag. Use a fraction and words to describe the probability of each outcome.

1. Picking a square _____

   _____

2. Picking a circle _____

   _____

3. Picking a rectangle _____

4. Picking a triangle _____

   _____

5. Picking a square or triangle _____

   _____

Spiral Review
Describe the probability of each outcome. Use *certain, likely, equally likely, unlikely,* or *impossible.*
(Lesson 16–1)

6. If Patricia picks out 1 fruit without looking, what is the probability that she will pick an apple? _____

7. If Jane picks out a fruit without looking, what is the probability that she will pick a banana? _____

8. If Mike picks out a fruit without looking, what is the probability that he will pick an orange? _____

Name _____ Date _____

Problem-Solving Practice

Probability and Fractions

Use the spinner to solve.

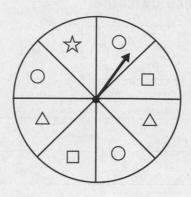

1. Rita and Jose are playing a game. They decide that the first person to land on the star will go first. What is the probability of landing on the star? Express the probability as a fraction.

_____

2. Rita and Jose take turns using the spinner. The first person to land on all four shapes wins the game. Rita goes first. What is the probability that she will land on a circle?
Express the probability as a fraction.

_____

3. Jessica and Bianca are playing a game. Each player has to name the shape she thinks she will land on before spinning. Bianca thinks she will land on a triangle. What is the probability that she will land on the triangle? Express it as a fraction.

_____

4. Jessica thinks she will land on a square. What is the probability that she will land on a square? Express it as a fraction.

_____

5. Simon and Luis are playing a game using the spinner. If the object of the game is to land on each shape before the other player, what shape would be the most difficult to land on?

_____

Express the probability of landing on that shape as a fraction.

_____

6. Simon goes first. What shape is he most likely to land on?

_____

Express the probability as a fraction.

_____

Name _____   Date _____

Homework Practice

Problem-Solving Strategy

Solve. Use the *make an organized list* strategy.

1. Koko has red shorts and blue shorts, and a print shirt, a T-shirt, or a tank top to wear. How many different outfits can he choose from?

   _____

2. Parker is handing out snacks. He has a large bag that is filled with smaller snack-sized bags. There is one bag of each of the following: peanuts, almonds, walnuts, mixed nuts, macadamia nuts, and cashews. What is the probability of picking a bag of macadamia nuts or almonds? How about cashews, almonds, or peanuts?

   _____

3. Martin's older brother wanted to buy a leather bomber jacket. It cost $190. He makes $38 each weekend mowing lawns and weeding gardens for neighbors. How many weekends will he need to work in order to buy the jacket?

   _____

4. Your teacher has 3 different stickers she can choose from including smiley faces, animals, or hearts. What is the probability of her choosing a heart if she picks one without looking?

   _____

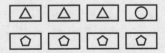 **Spiral Review**   **One shape is picked. Use words and a fraction to describe the probability of each outcome. Use *certain, likely, equally likely, unlikely,* or *impossible.* (Lesson 16-2)**

△	△	△	○
⬠	⬠	⬠	⬠

5. Picking a triangle?

   _____

16-4

Homework Practice

4SDAP2.1, 4SDAP2.2

Find Probability

The grid shows the outcomes of two spinners. Use the grid to answer each question.

	Second Spinner Outcomes			
First Spinner Outcomes	**1**	**2**	**3**	**4**
1	1,1	1,2	1,3	1,4
2	2,1	2,2	2,3	2,4
3	3,1	3,2	3,3	3,4
4	4,1	4,2	4,3	4,4

1. How many possible outcomes are there? _____

2. How many outcomes contain a pair of the same number? _____

3. What is the probability of spinning two numbers that total 4? _____

4. What is the probability of spinning two numbers that have a

product of 6? _____

5. What is the probability of an outcome that contains the number 1?

_____

6. What is the probability of spinning two numbers that are both

greater than 2? _____

Spiral Review

You pick one card. Use a fraction and words to describe the probability of each outcome. (Lesson 16-3)

△ △ △ ○ ○

⬠ ⬠ ⬠ ⬠ ○

7. Picking a pentagon? _____

_____

233

Name _____ Date _____

Problem-Solving Practice

Find Probability

Use the spinner to solve.

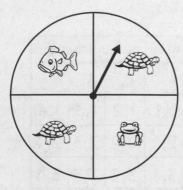

1. Mr. Avery has a nature game in his classroom. The game has a spinner with a fish, a frog, and 2 turtles. Paco uses the spinner to make predictions. If Paco spins the spinner 100 times, what is a reasonable prediction of the number of times that he will land on a fish?

   _____

2. If Paco spins the spinner 50 times, what is a reasonable prediction of the number of times that he will land on a turtle?

   _____

3. Jerome uses the nature spinner to make predictions. If Jerome spins the spinner 100 times, what is a reasonable prediction of the number of times that he will land on a turtle?

   _____

4. If Melanie spins the spinner 50 times, what is a reasonable prediction that it will land on a frog or a fish?

5. Maggie is conducting an experiment with the nature spinner. If Maggie spins the spinner 100 times, what is a reasonable prediction of the number of times that she will land on a turtle or a frog?

   _____

6. Maggie will spin the spinner 50 times. She predicts that the spinner will land on the frog about 12 times. Is her prediction reasonable? _____ Explain your thinking.

   _____

   _____

   _____

   _____

   _____

   _____

Name _____ **Date** _____

Homework Practice

4MR1.1, 4NS3.0

Problem-Solving Investigation

Solve using any strategy shown below.

- Use logical reasoning
- Work backward
- Make a model
- Make an organized list
- Draw a picture

1. Sydney is a receptionist and needs to make 28 phone calls. If she can make 4 phone calls in an hour, will she be able to make all of her calls in an 8 hour day? If so, how many additional phone calls will she be able to make? _____

2. Wanda rides her bike to and from school 5 days a week. She rides $\frac{3}{4}$ mile one way. How many miles will she bike in 1 week? 2 weeks?

_____

3. Nora made 4 photo albums the first year, 4 photo albums the second year, 3 photo albums the third year, and 3 photo albums the fourth year. If the pattern continues, how many photo albums will she make the fifth and sixth years? _____

4. Lola can choose from a blue sweatshirt, brown sweatshirt, or green sweatshirt, with brown boots, black boots, or tennis shoes. How many combinations can she wear? _____

Spiral Review The grid shows the possible outcomes of tossing a coin and spinning a spinner. Use the grid to answer the questions. (Lesson 16–4)

Coin Flips	Spinner Outcomes		
	Red	Blue	Green
Heads	H, Red	H, Blue	H, Green
Tails	T, Red	T, Blue	T, Green

5. How many possible outcomes are there? _____

6. What is the probability that you will flip a heads and spin a red or blue? _____

7. What is the probability that you will spin a red and flip a tails? _____

Name _____ Date _____

Homework Practice

Tree Diagrams

Draw a tree diagram.

1. What is the probability of choosing a white jacket and black shoes?

Jacket	Shoes
White	Black
Black	Tan
Green	White

Spiral Review

For Exercises 2–4, use the chart below. (Lesson 16–5)

Sandcastle-Building Contests

Location	Number of People
Port Aransas, TX	1,250
Wenatchee, WA	1,675
Seal Beach, CA	1,775
Atlantic City, NJ	1,525
Malibu, CA	1,375

2. What location had the greatest number of people at the
   sandcastle-building contest? _____

3. What location had the least number of people?

   _____

4. What was the difference in the number of people at the two
   California locations? _____

Name _____ Date _____

Problem-Solving Practice

Tree Diagrams

Make a tree diagram to solve.

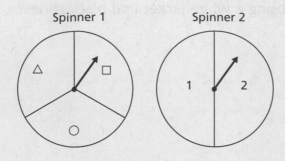

Spinner 1   Spinner 2

1. Jared and Dimitri are playing a game with 2 spinners. How many possible combinations are there if Dimitri spins both spinners?

   _____ possible combinations

2. Anna is deciding what she could wear to the zoo tomorrow. She can choose a white shirt, a green shirt, or a blue shirt. She can choose blue pants or green pants. How many different outfits can she make? _____ possible outfits

   What are they?